S. Ian. D. McKee

c/o. UNDP
  P O BOX No 224
  RAMNA
  DACCA
  BANGLADESH

New England Prospect

125 [**Painted Fireboard with a View of Beverly**] Unknown artist;
Salem, Massachusetts, circa 1818–1820.

New England Prospect

A Loan Exhibition of Maps
at
The Currier Gallery of Art

MANCHESTER, NEW HAMPSHIRE

Peter Benes

PUBLISHED BY BOSTON UNIVERSITY
FOR THE DUBLIN SEMINAR FOR NEW ENGLAND FOLKLIFE

This exhibition and accompanying catalogue have been prepared for The Currier Gallery of Art by the Dublin Seminar for New England Folklife, Dublin, New Hampshire, with support from the National Endowment for the Humanities, Washington, D.C., a federal agency, and the New Hampshire Commission on the Arts.

Copies are available by mail from Boston University Scholarly Publications, 985 Commonwealth Avenue, Boston, Mass. 02215. Price $10 each, plus $.50 postage and handling charge per copy.

Dates of the exhibition: June 21–September 2, 1980
The Currier Gallery of Art, Manchester, New Hampshire

Library of Congress Catalog Card Number 81-72021

ISBN 87270-019-4

Designed by Jerome Schuerger

The Dublin Seminar for New England Folklife is a continuing series of conferences, exhibitions, and publications designed to explore everyday life, work, and culture in New England's past. Offered in conjunction with the Program in American and New England Studies, Boston University, the series focuses attention on emerging areas of folk studies, regional and local history, cultural geography, social history, historical archeology, vernacular arts, material culture, and antiquarian studies. The Dublin Seminar for New England Folklife was chartered as a nonprofit corporation in the State of New Hampshire in 1978. Address enquiries to the Director, The Dublin Seminar for New England Folklife, Dublin, New Hampshire 03444.

Foreword

Exhibitions are, by their very nature, ephemeral. Therefore it is particularly gratifying to us that the "New England Prospect" exhibition, held at The Currier Gallery of Art in the summer of 1980, has been commemorated in a richly illustrated and carefully documented catalogue that effectively recaptures some of the show's visual excitement and intellectual fascination.

The immediate impact of the exhibition derived from the fact that it brought together a unique body of cartographic material, some of which had lain concealed for generations — even centuries — in state archives and similarly forbidding repositories. Viewers were given an opportunity to establish relationships between this material, to compare printed survey maps with hand-drawn memory maps, and to examine long established documents in the light of newly discovered ones — for example, the noted 1728 Burgis map of Boston with John Smibert's recently unearthed 1738 *vew of Boston.* Some of the inferences to be drawn from a critical scrutiny of this material are put forth in Peter Benes's enlightening introductory essay. We trust that the existence of this catalogue will allow continued discussion and examination of the material at hand, and encourage further research and discovery in what promises to be a richly rewarding field of scholarly activity.

An exhibition and catalogue of this size, complexity, and expense clearly represent a collaborate effort. We are especially grateful to Peter Benes for conceiving the idea, supervising the search for material, writing the catalogue introduction, and — with his wife Jane Benes — preparing the catalogue copy. We wish to thank Alan Grimard, Richard Ayer, and Philip Zimmerman of The Currier Gallery of Art for their help in arranging the exhibition; Pat Mahon of Boston University Publications Production for shepherding the catalogue through production; and Jerome Schuerger of Boston University's Graphic Design department for his design. We also wish to thank the New Hampshire Commission on the Arts for a grant to help underwrite the exhibition.

Both exhibition and catalogue were financed by a grant from the National Endowment for the Humanities. We are extremely grateful to the N.E.H., not only for its financial support, but for the guidance and advice of its staff. At a time when federal funding for such projects is being drastically curtailed, we, are acutely aware of its usefulness, thankful for its continuation, and sensitive to our obligation to make every last penny count.

Robert M. Doty, Director
The Currier Gallery of Art

Patrick Gregory, Supervisor
Boston University
Scholarly Publications

DETAIL 67 **Providence 1790** John Fitch; Rhode Island, 1790.

Contents

Lenders to the Exhibition

AMERICAN ANTIQUARIAN SOCIETY
BEDFORD HISTORICAL SOCIETY
PAUL BERNHEIMER'S ANTIQUE ARTS
THE BOSTONIAN SOCIETY
BOSTON PUBLIC LIBRARY
JOHN CARTER BROWN LIBRARY, BROWN UNIVERSITY
RICHARD M. CANDEE
CHILDS GALLERY
THE CONNECTICUT HISTORICAL SOCIETY
CONNECTICUT STATE ARCHIVES
DARTMOUTH COLLEGE LIBRARY
JOHN S. du MONT
ESSEX INSTITUTE
EXETER PUBLIC LIBRARY
FAIRFIELD HISTORICAL SOCIETY
THE HENRY WHITFIELD HOUSE
WOOD MEMORIAL LIBRARY
HISTORICAL SOCIETY OF OLD NEWBURY
LEMPSTER HISTORICAL SOCIETY
LIBRARY OF THE BOSTON ATHENAEUM
LIBRARY OF CONGRESS
LITCHFIELD HISTORICAL SOCIETY
MAINE HISTORICAL SOCIETY
MAINE STATE MUSEUM
MARBLEHEAD HISTORICAL SOCIETY
MASSACHUSETTS HISTORICAL SOCIETY
NEW ENGLAND HISTORIC GENEALOGICAL SOCIETY
NEW HAMPSHIRE HISTORICAL SOCIETY
NEW HAMPSHIRE STATE LIBRARY
NEWPORT HISTORICAL SOCIETY
PILGRIM HALL
RHODE ISLAND HISTORICAL SOCIETY
THE SOCIETY FOR THE PRESERVATION OF NEW ENGLAND
ANTIQUITIES
UNIVERSITY OF VERMONT, GUY W. BAILEY LIBRARY
YALE UNIVERSITY LIBRARY
YARMOUTH HISTORICAL SOCIETY
PRIVATE COLLECTIONS

Acknowledgments

This exhibition and catalogue were made possible through the cooperative efforts of numerous individuals and institutions. Foremost among these have been the National Endowment for the Humanities, for support in both the planning and implementation phases of the project, and Jessie Lie and Daniel Farber, Worcester, Mass., who for the second time in as many years contributed their time and resources to loan exhibitions organized by the Dublin Seminar. Mr. and Mrs. Farber photographed the maps that could not be borrowed for the exhibition and provided the negatives and prints for many of the maps illustrated in this catalogue as well as the superb photograph of the painted fireboard view used for the cover. Of equal importance were the contributions of Arthur J. Krim of the Massachusetts Historical Commission and John R. Stilgoe of the Department of Visual and Environmental Studies at Harvard University, who helped research and plan the exhibition and the Dublin Seminar conference that accompanied it; and of Robert M. Doty, Director, and Philip D. Zimmerman, Curator, The Currier Gallery of Art, who were responsible for the exhibition installation. The Currier Gallery also generously provided facilities for the exhibition and for two of the five conference sessions.

Other individuals also made important contributions. Bettina A. Norton, Essex Institute, gave many hours of research and writing toward the preparation of the exhibition labels. Her efforts were supplemented by William Copeley, Associate Librarian, New Hampshire Historical Society; Brian Burford, New Hampshire Land Surveyors' Association; and Mary Emhardt, Barrington, N.H. Edwin A. Churchill, Maine State Museum, generously provided ethnohistorical research and consulting. The project goals were enlarged and refined by Richard M. Candee, Boston University, who also made important discoveries in the search for vernacular maps. Robert M. Campbell, Dover, Mass., and Stewart McHenry, Charlotte, Vt., made helpful contributions to the planning sessions. The exhibition search was assisted by Philip Zea, Historic Deerfield; Russell Handsman, American Indian Archeological Institute; Robert Emlen, Rhode Island Historical Society; Alexandra Grave, Guilford, Conn.; Patricia Devoe, Scotland, Conn.; and Ethel and Richard A. Montague, Chatham, Mass. Dr. Albert Whitaker, Interim Archivist at the Massachusetts Archives, generously permitted the photography of documents under his care at the Massachusetts State House. Samuel Spiker, John McCann, James R. Killian, and Polaroid Corporation helped secure photographic reproductions of two maps at the Massachusetts Archives. Special mention must be given to the New Hampshire Historical Society, the principal lender to the exhibition, for the support received from John F. Page, Director, and James L. Garvin, Curator. Special acknowledgment, too, is due to the Essex Institute for permission to use the Beverly fireboard on the cover.

In addition, the contributions of the following individuals and institutions were essential to the success of this project: Jeannette D. Black, Susan L. Danforth, Thomas R. Adams, Andrew Oliver, and Augustus P. Loring, John Carter Brown Library, Brown University; Laura Monti and Sinclair H. Hitchings, Boston Public Library; Georgia B. Bumgardner and Marcus McCorison, American Antiquarian Society; Rodney Armstrong, Pamela Hoyle, and Lisa Backman, Library of the Boston Athenaeum; Laurence R. Pizer and Jeanne M. Mills, Pilgrim Hall; Frederick S. Allis, Jr., Colonial Society of Massachusetts; Richard Stephenson, John A. Wolter, and Jon D. Freshour, Library of Congress; Ellie Reichlin, Carolyn Hughes, and Brock W. Jobe, the Society for the Preservation of New England Antiquities; Thomas L. Gaffney, Maine Historical Society; Thomas G. Brennan and Helen Kebabian, Rhode Island Historical Society; Robert Claus and Eunice G. DiBella, Connecticut State Archives; J. Kevin Graffagnino, Guy W. Bailey

Library, University of Vermont; Bryant F. Tolles, Jr., Anne Farnam, and Robinson Murray, Essex Institute; Wilhelmina V. Lunt, Historical Society of Old Newbury; Avis Duckworth, New Hampshire State Library; Mrs. James W. Griswold and Mrs. Edward T. Veale, Exeter Public Library; Thomas Wendell Parker, the Bostonian Society; Rutherford D. Rogers, Barbara B. McCorkle, and Stephen L. Peterson, Yale University Libraries; Robert Egleston, New Haven Colony Historical Society; Marjorie Trotman, Friends of the Wood Memorial Library, South Windsor, Conn.; Kenneth C. Cramer, Baker Memorial Library, Dartmouth College; Dorothy Armistead, Henry Whitfield Museum; Christopher Nevins, Fairfield Historical Society; James B. Bell and Michael Gorn, New England Historic Genealogical Society; W. T. Holmes, Newport Historical Society; Bertram K. and Nina Fletcher Little; Paul Bernheimer's Antique Arts; the Reverend Hugh S. Clark, Yarmouth Historical Society; Randy Cotton, Lempster Historical Society; Mrs. A. H. Webber, Beverly Historical Society; Carl L. Crossman and D. Roger Howlett, Childs Gallery; John R. Merrow and Mrs. Gregory Smith, Marblehead Historical Society; Barbara B. MacDonald, Litchfield Historical Society; Mrs. E. P. Friedland, Thompson R. Harlow, and Christopher P. Bickford, Connecticut Historical Society; Louis L. Tucker and Ross Urquhart, Massachusetts Historical Society; Doris Peck, Bedford Historical Society; Donald T. Gibbs, Redwood Library; Aileen Loring and Diane Lothrop, Office of the Plymouth County Commissioners; Barry B. Tracy, Metropolitan Museum of Art; John Powers, Suffolk Superior Court, Boston; Samuel Silsby, Maine State Archives; Helmuth W. Joel, Jr., Dublin School; Jonathan Fairbanks, Museum of Fine Arts, Boston; David D. Hall, Boston University; Nancy Heyl, Exeter Historical Society; Donald C. O'Brien, Pontiac, Michigan; Charles Hammond, Gore Place Society, Waltham, Mass.; Connecticut Historical Commission; Harvard Map Collection, Pusey Library; and Eleanor Bellows Cochrane, Dublin, N.H.

The installation of the exhibition received assistance from the New Hampshire Commission on the Arts. The writing of the catalogue was made possible in part through a year's residence at the Concord Antiquarian Museum, Concord, Mass. Jane M. Benes generously assisted in all phases of the exhibition and catalogue preparation.

Peter Benes
Concord, Massachusetts
June 1981

List of Exhibited Maps, Views, and Surveying Instruments

I The New England Region
1 *Norvmbega et Virginia* Cornelius Wytfliet, 1597
2 *la Nouelle franse* Samuel de Champlain, 1613
3 *New England Observed* John Smith, 1614
4 *Niev Nederlandt* Adriaen Block, circa 1614
5 *The South part of New-England* William Wood, 1634
6 *Nova Belgica et Anglia Nova* Willem Blaeu, 1635
7 *totius Novi Belgii in America* Tobias Lotter, circa 1740
8 *A Mapp of New England* John Seller, 1676
9 *A Map of New-England* John Foster, 1677
10 *Description of New England* William Hack, circa 1695
11 *An Exact Mapp of New England and New York* Robert Morden, 1702
12 *the most Inhabited part of New England* Braddock Mead, 1755 (Jefferys, 1774)
13 *the most Inhabited part of New England* Braddock Mead, 1755 (Le Rouge, 1777)

II Colonies, Counties, and Coastlines
14 *Massachusetts in N. Englande* John Winthrop, circa 1633
15 *Pascatway River in New England by I:S:*, circa 1660
16 *Mapp of the Eastern Countrey* William Pitkin, circa 1691
17 *Limits of the Colony of Rhoad Island* John Mumford, 1720
18 *Connecticut and Rhode Island* Thomas Kitchin, 1758
19 *Eben^r. Smiths Map* Ebenezer Smith, 1780
20 *A Map of the District of Maine* Osgood Carleton, 1795
21 *A Map of Essex County* Anna Peabody, circa 1830
22 *Connecticut* Clara B. Shattuck, circa 1835

III Boundary Surveys and Disputes
23 *the Bounds of Massechusets Bay Patent* Nathaniel Woodward and Solomon Saffery, 1642
24 *the Pequids, theire Country* Uncas, 1662
25 Boundaries of Massachusetts, William Stoughton and Peter Bulkeley, circa 1677
26 *A Map of the Towns of Hattfield, Hadley*, 1709
27 Mason's Curve Line, mid-eighteenth century
28 *the Sea Coast of New England*, 1738
29 Merrimack and Piscataqua Rivers, circa 1726
30 *Plan*, circa 1750
31 *A Plan of the Rivers* George Mitchell, 1739
32 *the Boundary Line between the Commonwealth . . . and the State* Caleb Butler, 1825

IV Town Surveys
33 *Chelmsford* John Sherman, 1656
34 *Towneship of Squnshapag* Joshua Fisher, 1667
35 *Bounds of the town of weare* Joseph Baker, 1749
36 Haverhill, Massachusetts, after 1769
37 *Louden, October 30 1794* Joab Griswold, 1794
38 *A Plan of the Town of Sherburn*, 1794
39 *An Accurate Map of the Town* Richard Emerson, 1805
40 *Plan of Deerfield*, 1805

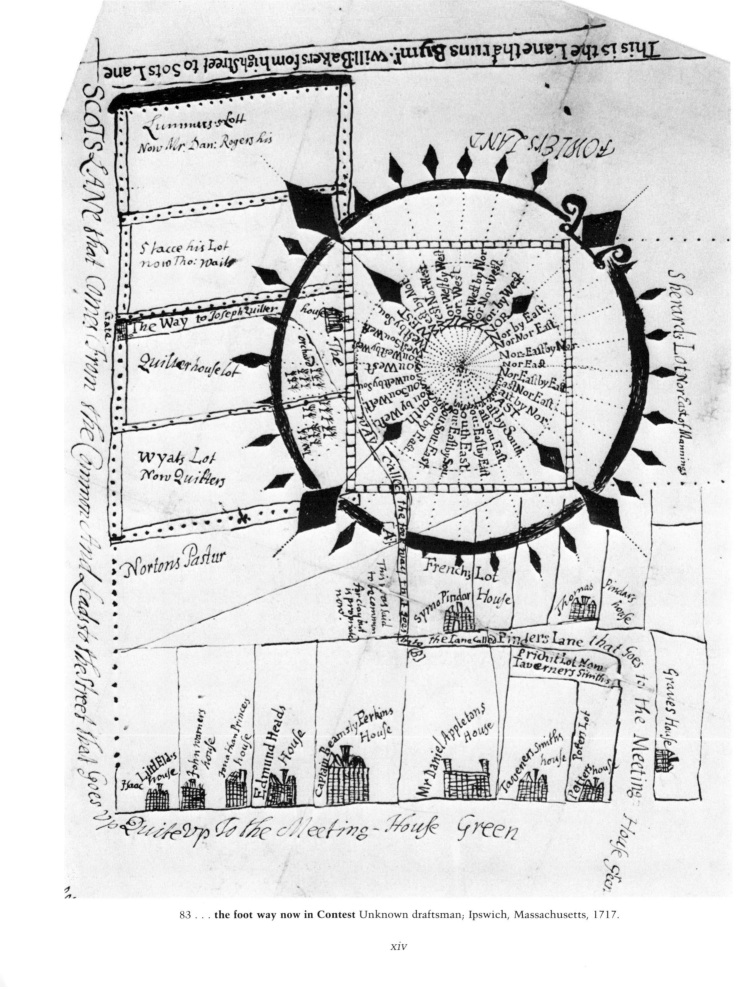

83 . . . **the foot way now in Contest** Unknown draftsman; Ipswich, Massachusetts, 1717.

Introduction

New England Prospect

*Maps, Place Names,
and the Historical Landscape*

W HEN WILLIAM WOOD published *Nevv Englands Prospect* in London in 1634, he promoted the book in the usual expansive manner of the seventeenth century. The work was, as he expressed it,

> A true, lively, and experimentall description of that part of *America,* commonly called NEVV ENGLAND: discovering the state of that Countrie, both as it stands to our new-come *English* Planters; and to the old Native Inhabitants.

The goals of the 1980 exhibition *New England Prospect: Maps, Place Names, and the Historical Landscape,* whose title was drawn from Wood's history, aspired to those of his subtitle. It was indeed an "experimentall" approach to local and regional history, which attempted to discover "the state of that Countrie" through maps and views chosen for cartographic, historical, decorative, or social significance. The exhibition was developed as the focus for a three-day conference offered by the Dublin Seminar for New England Folklife in June 1980 at Dublin and Manchester, New Hampshire. Its larger conceptual purpose, however, was to demonstrate that the New England landscape, like an artifact, was defined by prevailing cultural attitudes and assumptions. The region's early topography was seen as reflecting the cummulative activities of people engaged in clearing fields, fencing off pasturelands, erecting stone walls, laying out roads, and building millponds and meetinghouses. The exhibition attempted to recover and re-create these activities and to document the larger "folk" process of landscape making and landscape naming as it evolved in the region from 1500 to 1850 when European immigrants absorbed and replaced the Algonquian culture existing around them with English toponymic and agricultural traditions.

The exhibition also attempted to explore the intellectual and cultural matrix in which these processes took place. What was the extent of map literacy in the region before 1850? Were there aesthetic components to this literacy? What were the relationships between colonial American and European mapmaking and naming traditions, both aristocratic and vernacular, as well as between colonial American and Algonquian mapmaking and naming traditions? To answer these questions, the exhibition planners were obliged to go beyond the usual repertory of printed maps associated with well-known events and to explore a body of peripherally known vernacular or "folk" documents that were the product of everyday people who lived below the level of historical scrutiny. These latter documents were the subject of a systematic eighteen-month search and occupied the largest share of the time and energies of the project coordinators. In taking this approach, the exhibition planners were confronted with an unforeseen paradox. On the one hand, the search gradually made clear that vernacular maps probably did not exist in any large numbers. An abstract, conceptual activity far removed from the experience of everyday people, mapping in the seventeenth and eighteenth centuries was a military and measuring activity dependent on a relatively high level of technical knowledge and aesthetically grounded in long-standing European aristocratic tastes. On the other hand, because a trained or professional tradition in map-making and cartography did not evolve in America before 1790, vernacular maps — perhaps more accurately termed "working maps" — were the only kind that did exist in New England for the first two hundred years of the region's history.

The search was thus based on two untested premises. The first was that a body of everyday or working maps was to be found in libraries, in museums, in map archives, or in private collections; the second was that, when uncovered, these maps would reveal important insights into the early toponymic and topographic evolution of the New England landscape. At times, the prospects for success were not encouraging. Because of their vulnerability to handling and to light, few cartographic documents have survived. Like early copies of the *New England Primer,* they became worn out by use or exposure and disintegrated. Many probably were discarded as obsolete. Those that survived tended to be special exceptions, often decorative or genealogical pieces preserved and handed down by successive generations. Additionally, a review of library collections and archives indicated that most extant working maps were lot plans — surveyors' area and course calculations that revealed little cultural, architectural, or topographic data.

In the end, a fortuitous combination of circumstances overcame these obstacles. The most important reason for the success of the search was the benefit it derived from a long-standing tradition of cartographic antiquarianism and scholarship in New England that helped provide a methodological framework within which the search was carried out. Beginning as early as 1636 when Governor John Winthrop responded to Robert Ryece's request to send to England a sketch plan of Massachusetts Bay, interest in maps has remained a lasting feature of the New England mind. Winthrop's interest resurfaced in the person of Cotton Mather, who as a young man prepared a map of the region that regrettably has been lost. It resurfaced again in the person of James Wadsworth, a young Yale graduate destined to become a general in the Revolutionary War, who in 1748 drew a "memory map" of New Haven that served as a prototype of many similar town plans made in New England. This tradition was continued by the eighteenth-century historian and minister Ezra Stiles, who filled his notebooks with cartographic sketches and gleanings from oral history. In the early nineteenth century the Massachusetts Historical Society uncovered and published a drawing of the 1666 deed map in the Plymouth Colony archives prepared by Sassamon, King Philip's secretary. In the 1830s and 1840s John Warner Barber, a New Haven artist and historian whose perception of the past, like that of Ezra Stiles, was grounded in a systematic accumulation of local detail, again published the Sassamon map among his views of Massachusetts towns. Cartographic scholarship reached a high point in the late nineteenth century with Justin Winsor, for many years head of the Boston Public Library, whose knowledge of maps and early history of the New World and New England may never be equaled. Winsor's eight-volume *Narrative and Critical History of America* and four-volume *Memorial History of Boston,* published in the 1880s, reflect a lifetime of interest in New England and American mapping and for the first time reproduced numerous maps known only in their original states in European or American libraries. During the same decade Henry F. Waters of the Massachusetts Historical Society discovered the 1633 Winthrop map in the collection of the British Museum. And in the following decade, the 1688 Phillip Wells map of Boston Harbor was discovered for sale in England and purchased privately on behalf of an American collector. More recently, I. N. Phelps Stokes, a print collector who left an important collection of maps to the New York City Public Library, compiled his six-volume *Iconography of Manhattan Island*, which included a detailed study of all the printed maps of New England and New England subjects then known. And on a regional basis, map bibliographies were compiled by Howard M. Chapin for Rhode Island and by Edmund Thompson for Connecticut. Even the anonymous compilers of the *List of Maps of Boston* — a little-known but important bibliography published in 1910 by the City of Boston Engineering Department — were part of this antiquarian and scholarly tradition and contributed measurably to the task at hand.

A second circumstance that contributed to the success of the search was that certain types of working maps — chiefly town maps and seventeenth-century land-grants surveys — had been assembled in state, municipal, and private archives. The single largest source of such maps was the Massachusetts Archives at the State House in Boston. As early as 1641, the Massachusetts General Court required newly chartered towns to submit plans of their boundaries; in 1794 and again in 1832 the state required all towns in the Commonwealth to prepare and submit measured surveys of their bounds on a scale of 200 rods to an inch for the purpose of compiling accurate maps of the state. The majority of these town maps, together with maps generated by boundary controversies adjudicated by the General Court, have survived and have been catalogued. Similar repositories exist in the Connecticut State Library, the New Hampshire State Library, the New Hampshire Historical Society, and the Maine State Archives. Equally important cartographic documents have survived as court records. The Superior Court of Suffolk County, Massachusetts, for example, which at one time had appeals jurisdiction over coastal towns in the District of Maine, has in its legal archives two volumes of maps submitted in litigation involving property boundaries. These volumes contain second- and third-generation clerks' copies of surveys like those by William Godsoe of Kittery. Some private historical societies have also accumulated important map archives. The collection at the New Hampshire Historical Society is one of the finest and includes numerous eighteenth-century proprietors' maps turned over to the Society by the State of New Hampshire. Comparable in quality are the collections at the Essex Institute and the Rhode Island Historical Society and at academic libraries such as those at Dartmouth College, Yale University, and the University of Vermont.

A third circumstance that helped the map search was the personalities of New Englanders themselves. To a greater or lesser degree, many of the land surveyors who produced the lot plans, town plans, and land division plans now in public and private archives gave in to an impulse to color, illustrate, decorate, or otherwise elaborate their work beyond the immediate needs of a legal document. In a real sense the looked-for vernacular or "folk" mapmakers in New England turned out to be land surveyors. Individuals such as William and John Godsoe of Kittery, or Joab Griswold of Hartford County, who were trained professional surveyors but who elaborated their work with illustrations of animals, reptiles, birds, trees, houses, ships, roadways, bridges, wells, mills, and meetinghouses, unconsciously expressed the values and viewpoints of common people in New England. It is to them that the search ultimately owes its success.

Time constraints prevented a systematic examination of at least two sources of maps. It can reasonably be assumed that the majority of New England maps — both printed and manuscript, particularly in the area of memory maps — have always been in private hands, either still owned by descendants of the makers or dispersed among collectors. With some important exceptions, which were included in the exhibition, these were beyond the reach of an eighteen-month search. A second unexplored source was deeds records at county or town archives. Here, too, the volume of these documents, which number in the tens of thousands, precluded a systematic search. It is with deeds and other legal and municipal sources, however, that the greatest potential still remains. The same sometimes frustrating circumstances that have kept legal documents from sharing the benefits of professional conservation also have prevented their dispersal into private ownership and consequent loss to scholarship.

ii

While conclusions are premature, a number of patterns have become manifest in the course of planning the exhibition and preparing this catalogue. A brief review of these will help put the individual entries into perspective. As a general rule, early New England mapping was functional rather than artistic. Even the most ambitious surveys and maps lacked the conventions, wit, artistry, and visual conceits that were common in the vocabulary of European and English engravers and mapmakers working under aristocratic patronage. *The figure of the Indians fort or Palizado,* drawn for an English audience by an English engraver — and using an unusual circumferential perspective — is the only artistically sophisticated map in the exhibition. By European standards, however, even this was likely to have been seen as crude and naive, appropriate to an American subject.

A specific correlation exists between New England mapping and the expression or resolution of power conflicts. Indeed, until the emergence of decorative maps and "memory maps" in the eighteenth and nineteenth centuries, virtually all mapmaking and map patronage in New England society was a function of territorial controversy or the extension or consolidation of land tenure. This correlation can be seen in both general and particular terms. The two periods of most active New England mapmaking coincided with King Philip's War (1675–1676) and the American Revolution (1775–1783). War-related place names and features of maps produced in 1675 and 1676 remained part of the vocabulary of printed maps of New England for decades after the end of King Philip's War. Massachusetts, an aggressive, contentious colony throughout the seventeenth and eighteenth centuries, generated more maps than any other New England colony and probably more than any of the fifteen northern American colonies before 1775. By contrast, Rhode Island, whose ambitions were simply to survive under its own jurisdiction, produced almost no maps at all and only did so in an attempt to resist encroachments by Connecticut and Massachusetts. Any controversy that involved distance, space, and position generated mapping: the location of meetinghouses, ownership and bounds of land, rights-of-way, parish and town jurisdictions, proprietors' divisions, fencing obligations, estate settlements, colony boundaries, siege-works, battles, or skirmishes. All were common subjects of surveys and maps; all involved struggle, dispute, or control of one form or another; each constitutes a particular genre of New England mapping. It came as no surprise, therefore, that the search uncovered no Algonquian maps of New England subjects; few, if any, ever existed. Places were conceived verbally by native Americans, and distances and spatial measurements were communicated entirely by toponymic relationships. King Philip cited the principal "names" of the land he was willing to sell in 1666, not the bounds or limits. Those few maps prepared in collaboration with Algonquian informants were conceptually English and European and were drawn by Englishmen or by natives trained under Englishmen.

Another pattern that emerged is the "copy" phenomenon. It would be only mild exaggeration to state that every document described in this catalogue is a copy of another document, either in the form of a copperplate print, a period manuscript copy, an out-of-period manuscript copy, a historical photograph, or a present-day photograph. Many copies are two or more stages removed from an original; others are one of a number of identical or closely related "original" manuscripts made by the same individual. Several of the brilliant Godsoe maps have survived only as copies by the Kittery town clerk who entered them routinely into the town record book or as copies of the town clerk's copies on file in the Suffolk County Superior Court in Boston. The Stoughton-Bulkeley and Woodward-Saffery maps, which number among the half dozen most important maps of the seventeenth century, are themselves copies or have survived only in copied form. Even a map as well known as James Wadsworth's 1748 *Plan of the Town of New Haven*, which was in its maker's possession in the early nineteenth century, is now known only from two manuscript copies made about 1800 and an engraved print produced in 1806. So frequently were maps copied that the traditional distinction between manuscript maps and printed maps at times becomes blurred. The survival in manuscript form of two almost identical right-of-way controversy maps involving Ipswich center in 1717 suggests that a number of copies of this document had been made and circulated by townspeople petitioning the Ipswich court for the privilege of crossing over private land. Conversely, later states of the printed 1614–1639 Smith map of New England, like the Bonner-Price map of Boston, were so radically altered that they must be perceived as entirely new maps.

Repeated copying by hand had a noticeable influence on style. In the two 1717 Ipswich right-of-way maps cited above, architectural symbols and pictographs were abstracted to the point of assuming a calligraphic appearance. The houses are drawn and shaded by what appears to be a hurried, tired hand, and they have a penmanlike quality consistent with their being two of a dozen or more similar maps prepared by one of several clerks from an original. At times, mapmakers adopted curious combinations of manuscript and printing techniques in order to reduce their work. The map by Sabin Lewis of the Apponogue village complex in Warwick, Rhode Island, which numbered twenty in a series, has hand-drawn streets, shorelines, and bridges. Repeated elements such as two- or three-story houses, names of owners, and stores are hand-stamped from carved wooden blocks.

The calligraphic appearance of New England map symbols is related to the use of naive perspective techniques, particularly to what the exhibition coordinators called the "lay-down" technique of showing buildings, trees, and other landscape features. This centuries-old cartographic projection consisted of drawing familiar eye-level views of buildings (usually the view seen from the nearest street) laid down flat on a map for the purpose of identification. (In architectural terminology this is the superimposition of a building elevation on a topographic plan.) Used by almost every surveyor in New England, this mannerism was so unconsciously retained that it was advertised by a professional engraver in the early nineteenth century as an innovation deserving special mention. Amos Doolittle of New Haven, best known for his four historical prints illustrating the 1775 engagements at Concord and Lexington, noted on an 1812 map of New Haven:

> The buildings in this Plan are marked differently from what is customary. Instead of giving the ground-plot it was thought it would be more pleasing to have the elevation of the Front. In doing this care has been taken, not only to exhibit the proportions of each building, but likewise the exact number of its doors & windows.

In point of fact, Doolittle's "elevation[s] of the Front" were no different from those that had been drawn by surveyors and makers of memory maps in New England from the earliest period of settlement. Only military cartographers and a handful of surveyors trained in European techniques illustrated buildings as plans.

A final pattern that emerged in this study of New England maps is the survival of traditional English or European distances. An anonymous seventeenth-century commentator noted that "comfortable communion" among the inhabitants of newly established towns in the region would ideally be achieved by a plan

> square 6 miles eury waye. The houses orderly placed about the midst, especially the meetinghous, the wch we will suppose to be the center of the wholl circumference.

The six-mile-square or five-mile-square spatial definition and the related social and ecclesiastical bonds of the New England community survived almost intact throughout the pre-industrial period. All other things being equal, New Englanders were unwilling to travel more than three or three and a half miles to attend meetings on Thursdays and the Sabbath. If the distance was greater than that, a new society or parish would be formed however scant its population base. Even as late as 1790, the average area of ecclesiastic societies in six Connecticut counties was 25.1 square miles — or five miles square — a size that put its residents a maximum of three miles from the meetinghouse. All of the town and parish maps studied for this exhibition conform to this pattern.

These physical limits to New Englanders' political and social horizons found a direct parallel in New Englanders' perception of the landscape. Whereas a majority of householders after 1650 probably had among their papers maps depicting land-tenure rights or fencing obligations, maps and charts of areas that went beyond the immediate "three-mile limit" — those of William Wood and John Foster, or even those of Robert Morden or Braddock Mead, which were drawn primarily for European audiences — were probably rare. Instead, landscape features beyond the average New England farmer's or fisherman's immediate area of concern were probably perceived by him in verbal terms. Nearby points were associated with known people: "Woods his hole" or "Briant's point"; more remote areas were conceived in generalized terms such as "The Great River," "The Islands," and "The Bay." Distances were seen in terms of days of travel time, inns for overnight lodging, names of friends, or relatives to visit. The first Europeans to settle and develop northeastern America after 1600 thus adopted and continued a verbal pattern of landscape perception and identification already in existence with the Algonquian natives for generations. Often, the Algonquian vocabulary was discarded in favor of an English vocabulary as a "seal" or confirmation of English territorial control; but in an equal number of instances the existing Algonquian names were retained. In this sense, apart from food production and agricultural practices, linguistic and toponymic usages may be said to be one of the few elements of the Algonquian culture to have successfully survived the impact of European immigration to North America.

Catalogue of the Exhibition

Dimensions are given to the nearest one-eighth inch;
an asterisk (*) indicates the entry is not illustrated;
height dimensions are given first.

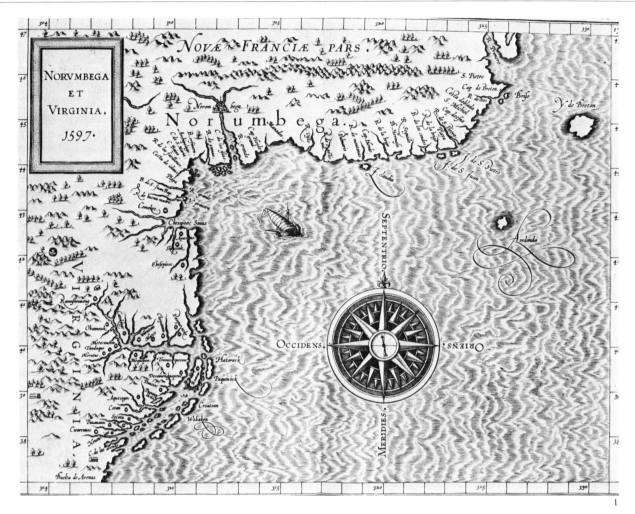

1

1

Norvmbega et Virginia

Cornelius Wytfliet (d. 1598)

Louvain, Netherlands, 1597

Engraving; 12¾ × 17 in.

Published in Wytfliet's *Descriptionis Ptolemaicae Augmentum*

Scale 1:8,700,000

John Carter Brown Library, Brown University

The earliest European name for New England was "Norumbega," whose origin and variant spellings "Norembega," "Norembeque," "Norombergue," "Nurumberg," "Noronbega," and "Moronbega" have perplexed lexicographers and geographers for more than four centuries. Considered by modern historians to be a fiction of the European imagination, the term has been linked with varying success to the Florentine navigator Giovanni da Verrazano's understanding of Penobscot or Narragansett Indian dialects and to the Latin name for Norway (*Norvegia*). But even in the late sixteenth century, when the Dutch atlas maker Cornelius Wytfliet

published the first volume of maps devoted to the Americas, he took pains to note that *Unde Norombegeae nomen regioni inditum sit, incertum est* (Where the name of Norumbega region was derived is uncertain).

A superbly executed engraving, Wytfliet's 1597 *Norvmbega et Virginia* depicts the northeastern American coastline as it was perceived by European geographers one hundred years after the discovery of the New World. Wytfliet's location of Norumbega as a landmass between "Novae Franciae Pars" and "Virginia," and as a walled city on a major river, marks the approximate high point in the toponymic evolution of Norumbega that began as a generic place name for all of north America and that ended up relegated to obscurity as the name for the Penobscot River in Maine. The descriptive literature of Norumbega was similarly ephemeral. Samuel Purchas noted in 1625:

> If this beautifull Towne Norumbega has ever been in nature, I would faine knowe who hath pulled it downe; for there is but Cabines heere and there made with pearkes, and covered with the barkes of

trees, or with skinnes, and both the River and the place inhabited is called Pemptegoet.

Peter Heylyn observed in 1652 that "far from being a fair City . . . there are only a few Sheds or Cabins covered with the barks of trees or the skins of beasts." By the time John Milton recorded "Norumbega and the Samoed shore" in *Paradise Lost* the name had lost its fabled associations and had disappeared from current maps and atlases.

Like all sixteenth-century delineations of the region, Wytfliet's New England excluded the Hudson and St. Lawrence rivers, Long Island, and Cape Cod. These were not correctly mapped until the voyages and discoveries of Samuel de Champlain, Adriaen Block, and John Smith in the early seventeenth century. Wytfliet's depiction of Virginia and the Hatteras shoreline, based on John White's 1590 map of Virginia, is more realistic.

References: McManis, 44–61; Ganong, "Origin"; Ganong, "Crucial"; Morison, 464–70; Winsor, *Narrative*, vol. 3; Tooley, 677; Heylyn, 4:107; Purchas, 18:243–44; Wytfliet, 184.

1 DETAIL illustrated p. 123.

2

Carte geographique de la Nouelle franse en son vray meridiein

Samuel de Champlain (1570–1635)

Paris, 1613

Engraving; 11 × 13¾ in.

Published in Champlain's *Les voyages du sieur de Champlain Xaintongeois*

Scale 1:7,000,000

Boston Public Library

The continued survival of "Norembeque" in seventeenth-century cartography is illustrated by a group of printed maps prepared by French explorers and colonizers of New France in the thirty-year period from 1603 to 1633. Samuel de Champlain, the French founder of Quebec and first governor of New France, was the author of many of these maps, but the names of Baron de Poutrincourt, Marc Lescarbot, and Francois Pontgrave — who accompanied Champlain at various times on his explorations — are also linked with them. These maps reflect increasing French familiarity with Labrador, Newfoundland, Acadia, and the Saint Lawrence River and estuary. They offered to Europeans the first realistic depiction of the

northeast American coastline and the Great Lakes.

Champlain's *Carte geographique de la Nouelle franse en son vray meridiein*, one of two maps of New France included in his 1613 *Les voyages du sieur de Champlain*, is characteristic of early forms of these maps and is the product of Champlain's explorations of interior Canada and the New England coast from 1603 to 1609, undertaken in search of a better and warmer colonizing site than Port Royal or Quebec. Prepared one year before Captain John Smith's *New England Observed* (3), it is clearly more accurate in the handling of the St. Lawrence River and the maritime region than it is of the New England coastline. Indeed, Cape Cod, called "C. mallebare," represents only a marginal improvement over sixteenth-century depictions. Nevertheless, Champlain sounded and left detailed charts of what are now Cape Ann, Plymouth, and Chatham harbors. His explorations south were frustrated by the number, sophistication, and aggressiveness of the Algonquians inhabiting the coast; this led him to remain in Quebec. Champlain's experience contrasted with

the abandoned villages found by Europeans a decade later after diseases had decimated the native population.

The place names on Champlain's map are principally in French with a few in Latin or English. At least one name is the engraver's transcription of what was probably a handwritten marginal comment on Champlain's manuscript: "the bay where hudson did Winter." Of Champlain's New England place names, only "quinibequy" (Kennebec) and "lac de Champlain" have survived; others such as "C. St. Loys," "C. de isles," "Charante," and "Choaloet" (some of which copy Wytfliet's designations) have not. Champlain's last maps, published a few years before his death in 1635, are much more accurate depictions of New England, notably Cape Cod, and include Long Island ("Isle de l'Ascension"). By this time, he or his engravers most likely had the benefit of Smith's and perhaps Block's maps of the coastline.

References: Fiske, 31–86; Paullin and Wright, 10–11; Cumming, "Charting," 74–77; Winsor, *Narrative,* 4:103–29; Winsor, *Memorial,* 1:47–49.

3

New England Observed and described by Captayn John Smith

John Smith (1580–1631), cartographer
Simon van de Passe, engraver
James Reeve, printer

London, 1627

Engraving; altered state of a 1616 plate; 11¾ × 14 in.

Published in Smith's *The Generall Historie of Virginia, New England and the Summer Isles*

Scale 1:970,000

American Antiquarian Society

The map that gave New England its name and that presented the first detailed view of the actual contours of eastern New England was drawn by Captain John Smith in 1614 following his six-month exploration of the area. (Only the Velasco map of 1610 pre-dated Smith's accurate delineation of the eastern coastline and Cape Cod.) Engraved in London by the Dutchman Simon van de Passe, *New England Observed and described by Captayn John Smith* first appeared in Smith's *Description of New England* published in London in 1616. It gained wide European exposure in subsequent publications such as John Smith's *New England and the Summer Isles* (1626), *Generall Historie of Virginia* (1627), and *Advertisements to unexperienced planters of New England* (1631). Ten states of the plate are known, the two major alterations being the rededication of the map to the "King of great Britaine" after Charles I's accession in 1625 and the addition of the arms of the Council of New England.

Beyond its major importance in establishing an accurate topographic image of New England in the European mind, Smith's *New England Observed* illustrates the role that printed maps — particularly those that enjoyed wide circulation — played in the naming of the American wilderness. Mindful of Spanish, French, and Dutch interests in the region, Smith Anglicized that part of America which, in his words, "hath formerly beene called Norumbega," substituting "New England" for this imprecise, and perhaps all-too-Spanish, term. Equally important, before passing the manuscript to his Dutch engraver, Smith presented it to "our most gracious King Charles, then Prince of Wales," who

was pleased to confirm it [New England] by that title, and did change the barbarous names of their principal harbors and habitations for such English, that posterity may say, King Charles was their godfather.

3

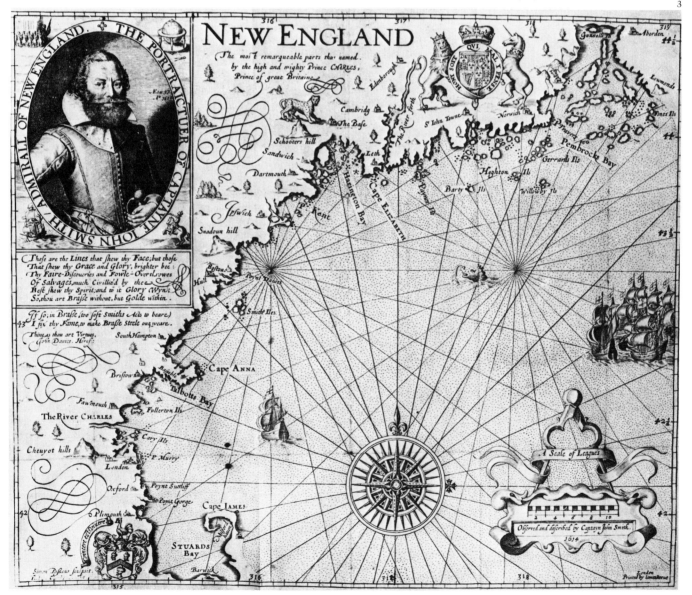

Accordingly, the young prince named "Cape James" (Cape Cod) after his father; "Stuarts Bay" (Cape Cod Bay) after the reigning family; "Cape Elizabeth" after his sister; "Cape Anna" after his mother; and "The River Charles" after himself. Only the latter three have survived. Others, including London, Oxford, Bristow, Fawmouth, and Boston, which were gratuitously and inaccurately inserted on the mainland, did not survive. Smith named the Isles of Shoals after himself. Even the London printer James Reeve got into the act by having a promontory on the Maine coastline named "Point Reeves."

Prints taken from later states of the plate corrected Smith's toponymic fiction. What has been identified as the ninth state, published four years after Smith's death as part of Wye Saltonstall's version of the Mercator-Hodius atlas, *Historia Mundi or Mercator's Atlas* (London, 1635), reveals the addition of ten actual New England towns, most of them accurately located: South Hampton (on the New Hampshire shoreline), Salem, Saugus, Charles Towne, Water towne, Boston, Dorchester, Roxderry [*sic*], Medford,

and New towne. To this extent, Smith's map, originally conceived as a sophisticated Flemish engraving, became a working document. Unlike the hundred-year Jansson-Visscher series of printed maps (6, 7), which perpetrated and in some instances compounded cartographic and toponymic inaccuracies for the amusement of European audiences, Smith's map served the readers of his publications by providing an up-to-date description of the New England region.

The importance of gratuitous but widely published place naming cannot be dismissed. To this day, historians do not know whether the Leyden pilgrims named their settlement because they landed at a spot marked "Plymouth" on John Smith's map (Governor William Bradford cited the map in his history of the plantation) or because the *Mayflower* embarked from the town of that name in Devonshire, England.

References: Bradford, 1:206–7; Winsor, *Memorial*, 1:50–56; McManis, 45; Chatterton, 240–41; Skelton, 63; Paullin and Wright, 10–11; Smith, John, 173; Boston, 6–14; Cumming, "Charting," 71–81.

3A DETAIL Smith, **New England Observed** 1631 state.

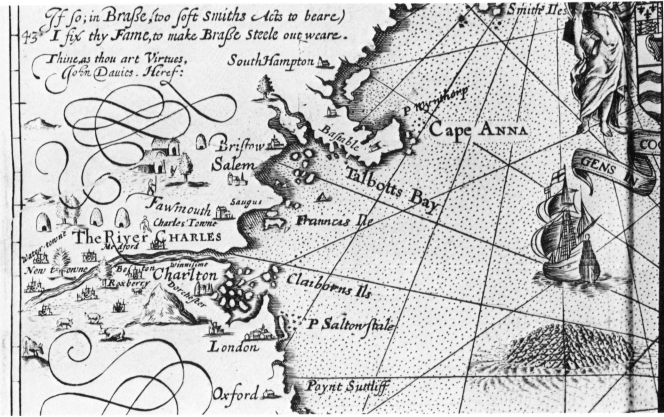

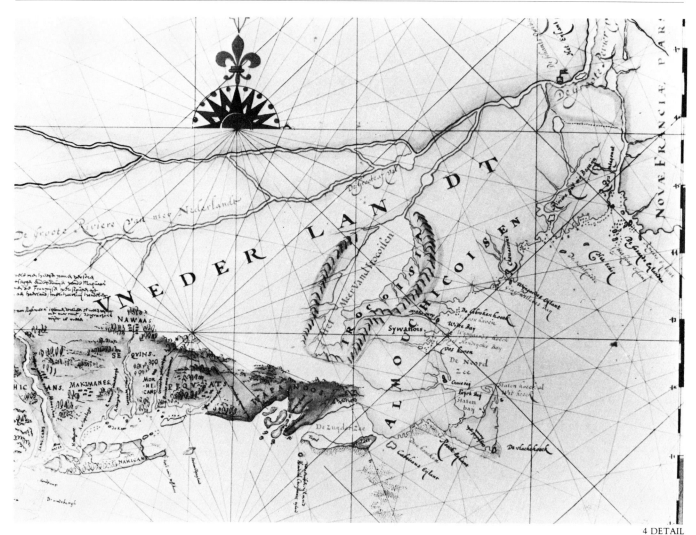

4 DETAIL

4

Niev Nederlandt

Adriaen Block

Netherlands, circa 1614

Chromolithograph by E. Spanier, The Hague, circa 1854; 30 × 22¾ in.

Facsimile of a manuscript, ink and watercolor

Scale 1:1,300,000

John Carter Brown Library, Brown University

The explorations in 1614 of Captain Andriaen Block of the Netherlands, which retraced the route followed by Giovanni da Verrazano in 1524, were the first serious challenge to French supremacy in the northeast region of North America by another European power. Prepared in 1614 and presented to the States General of the United Provinces in August 1616, Block's colored parchment map of the region combined Champlain's published discoveries with those of his own in the first truly accurate depiction of the coastlines of Long Is-

land, Connecticut, Rhode Island, and Narragansett Bay. Sixteenth-century "Norumbega" was renamed "Niev Nederlandt," with "Novae Franciae Pars" duly relegated to an area to the east of the Kennebec. The "Figurative Map," so called by the deputies of the United Company of Merchants for its accurate configuration of New England, was rediscovered in the archives of The Hague by an American historian in the mid-nineteenth century. Block's map, or manuscript copies of it, presumably had been known to early Dutch atlas makers and cartographers and through them gained wide circulation.

The two most serious errors made by Block in his handling of New England are the separation of Cape Cod from the mainland and the joining of Cape Cod, Martha's Vineyard, and Nantucket into a single landmass. Few mapmakers after Block depicted the Cape as an island; most cartographers, however, including William Wood (5) and Willem Janszoon Blaeu (6) were unaware of the insular nature of the landmasses south of the Cape

and unwittingly perpetuated Block's error. The "Dutch" plotting of Cape Cod was the accepted mode among cartographers until Nicolas Jansz Visscher separated the islands about 1650. The 1614–1616 Block map is a rich source of Algonquian tribal names before the intrusion of European culture. (Block Island he named for himself.) Puzzling, however, is Block's source for "Crane bay" (in what is now Plymouth Harbor), an apparent English place name with a brief history in the seventeenth century. Appearing on Peter Minuit's manuscript map of about 1630, Crane's Bay was published in Blaeu's 1635 *Nova Belgica* (6), as well as in John Seller's 1675 *New England* (8) and Hack's circa 1695 *Description of New England* (10), based on Seller. It then vanishes as mysteriously as it appeared in 1614.

References: Thompson, 9; Chapin, *Cartography;* Winsor, *Narrative,* 3:382, 4:433–36; Brodhead; Winsor, *Memorial,* 1:57–58; Cumming, "Charting," 81–82.

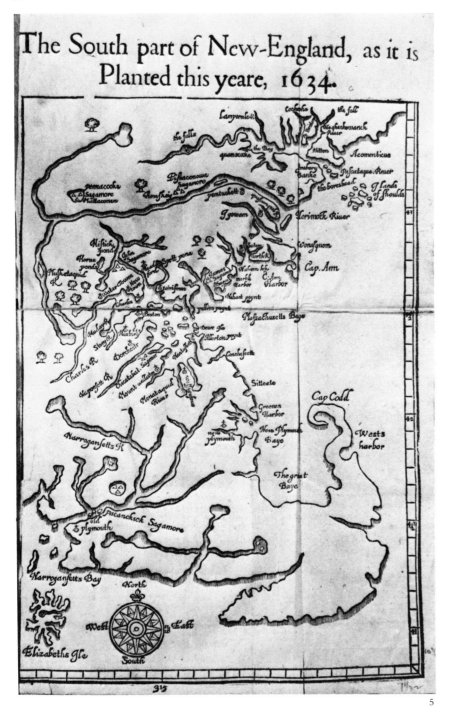

The South part of New-England, as it is Planted this yeare, 1634.

5

The South part of New-England, as it is Planted this yeare, 1634

William Wood (b. circa 1606)

New England and London, 1634

Woodcut; 10¾ × 7½ in.

Published in Wood's *Nevv Englands prospect*

Scale 1:1,500,000

Boston Public Library

William Wood's *South part of New-England*, a woodcut in part set with movable type, was printed before the founding of the English settlements on the Connecticut River and Long Island Sound. Prepared for Wood's 1634 *Nevv Englands Prospect*, it was the first printed map of the region by an English settler and the first to show Indian and English place names as they actually existed during the initial years of the Great Migration. No printed map of New England improved on Wood's *South part* until forty-three years later when John Fos-

ter prepared a woodcut map (9) based on boundary surveys commissioned by the Massachusetts Bay Colony. How much Wood relies on his personal observations and recordings and how much he obtained from second-hand sources such as Captain John Smith's map of 1614 (3) or Governor John Winthrop's map of 1633 (14) is open to question. His rendering of the tip of Cape Cod is clearly Smith's, and his rendering of the Merrimack and Musketaquid rivers conforms in conception to Winthrop's. But neither can by any means be regarded as a copy.

Like Block's "figurative" map (4), Wood's map follows the "Dutch" configuration of Cape Cod — joining Martha's Vineyard and Nantucket Island. (This error is also found on Robert Dudley's 1646 *Carta particolare della nuova Belgia.*) Wood's depiction and naming of Massachusetts Bay and the north shore, however — particularly the placing of the Indian villages "John Sagamore," "James Sagamore," and "Pissaconowa Sagamore" so close to the English settlements — illustrate the closeness of English and Algonquian life in the first decade of large-scale European settlement in the region.

Wood's map was immediately influential. The 1635 state of John Smith's map shows a number of accurately placed town names in the area of Massachusetts Bay that probably derived from Wood and additionally notes:

> He that desires to know more of the Estate of new England lett him read a new Book of the prospecte of new England & ther he shall have Satisfaction.

The borrowing may have gone both ways, however. Fictitious "Bristow," shown on Wood's map in the Piscataqua region, like "West's Harbor" on Cape Cod, were probably toponymic echoes of Smith.

William Wood was twenty-three when he came to America with his father, John Wood, in 1629 to help found the settlement at Lynn, Massachusetts (shown here as "Saugus"). Wood sailed back to England in 1634 to arrange the publication of his book. He returned to Lynn the following year and served as the town representative in the colony's General Court in 1636. In 1637 he led a group of Lynn residents to found the town of Sandwich on Cape Cod, but then he disappears from the printed records.

References: Wood, ii–iii; Boulind, 64; Boston, 14–16; Dudley; Tooley, 672; Winsor, *Memorial,* 1:524; Winsor, *Kohl,* 96; Cumming, "Charting," 80–81.

6

Nova Belgica et Anglia Nova

Willem Janszoon Blaeu (1571–1638)

Amsterdam, 1635

Engraving with watercolor; 15⅛ × 19¾ in. (image)

Published in Blaeu's *Atlas Appendix*

Scale 1:1,500,000

John Carter Brown Library, Brown University

7

Recens Edita totius Novi Belgii in America Septentrionali

Tobias Conrad Lotter, artist
Matthias Seutter (1678–1757), engraver

Augsburg, circa 1740

Engraving with watercolor; 19¼ × 22⅞ in.

Scale 1:2,000,000

New Hampshire Historical Society

Willem Blaeu's *Nova Belgica et Anglia Nova* (1635) and Tobias Conrad Lotter's *Recens Edita totius Novi Belgii* (circa 1740) represent the start and the end of a durable and highly artistic series of maps of New England and New York produced by Dutch, English, and German engravers and printers for cultivated Europeans. Beginning in the early seventeenth century as a relatively accurate synthesis of the geography of Samuel de Champlain, Adriaen Block, and John Smith, the so-called Jansson-Visscher series was continued into the eighteenth century as an artistic and professional tour de force by interconnected publishing and engraving families whose concern for accuracy became subservient to their overwhelming desire for pictographic and decorative clutter. The series perpetuated geographic, toponymic, and anthropological fictions about America. The value of these maps to historians comes

chiefly from the occasional realistic departures that engravers and publishers made from what was otherwise a stock fictional formula.

A Dutch maritime cartographer and atlas maker, Willem Janszoon Blaeu was a student of the astronomer Tycho Brahe and founder of a very successful printing house in Amsterdam. Published for the first time in his 1635 *Atlas Appendix*, Blaeu's *Nova Belgica et Anglia Nova* combined traditional perceptions of the New England coastline and Block's geography with selected elements of Smith's toponymy. "Norumbega," for example, which did not appear on Smith's map, has a subsidiary role as a river in Blaeu's Maine. A precursor to the Jansson-Visscher series, *Nova Belgica* displays at least four identifiable elements of the Jansson-Visscher formula: the triple, interconnected river system in the St. Lawrence River; the fusion of Lake

7

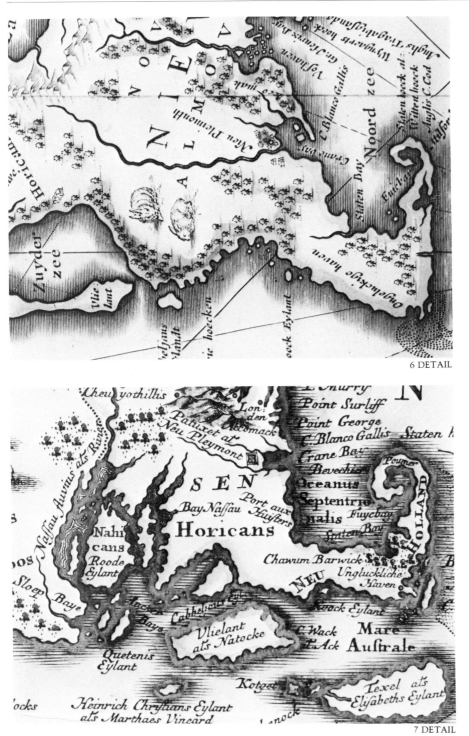

6 DETAIL

7 DETAIL

prominently placed an American turkey in eastern Connecticut; ignored the existence of the Merrimack River; and emptied Lake Winnipesaukee north into the St. Lawrence River. Tobias Lotter's richly colored *Recens Edita* represents the artistic and decorative climax of the Jansson-Visscher series. While still retaining Block's and Blaeu's long outdated cartographic formulas, the Lotter map multiplied many times the bestiary, increased the number and size of forests and mountain ranges, and developed a cartouche that crowded sixteen human figures and a superb view of seventeenth-century New York into the lower right-hand corner of the print.

Incredibly, many of Smith's place names appear intact on Lotter's map, sometimes with curious juxtapositions. London, Bristow, Carry Isles, Point George, Snowden Hill, Point Davis, Fullerton Isles, and Point Murry are all where John Smith and the young Charles Stuart put them in 1614. Smith's Cheuyot hills is "Cheuyothillis"; his Barwick is "Chawum Barwick"; his Fawmouth is "Totan Famouch"; his Dartmouth is "Buhanna Dantmont"; his Sandwich is "A good harbor Santwick." Perhaps most incredible of all is "Mr Pinsers Handel Hauss" on the Connecticut River, on the site of William Pynchon's trading outpost of 1636.

The last of the Jansson-Visscher publishers, Tobias Conrad Lotter took over the firm of his father-in-law, Matthias Seutter, after 1757 and probably had a hand in preparing the map illustrated here. Lotter continued to issue new states of the Seutter plate perhaps as late as 1781 — long after the appearance of accurate printed maps had made the Smith-Block-Blaeu fictions untenable.

References: Keuning; Campbell, "New Light"; Black, *Commentary,* 73–74; Stokes; Tooley, 61, 576–77; Cumming, "Charting," 81–84.

Champlain and Lake Winnipesaukee; the alternately rounded and rectangular palisaded Indian villages; and the absence of the Merrimack River. These features were imitated by the Amsterdam printer Jan Jansson who in 1651 prepared an engraving under the title *Belgii Novi, Angliae Novae, et Partis Virginiae.* Jansson widened the St. Lawrence River and added islands in it and in Lake Champlain/Winnipesaukee. *Belgii Novi* was the first of nine known copperplates, each with identifiable states, published by the Dutchmen Nicolas Jansz Visscher, Justus Danckers, Adriaen vander Donck, Hugo Allard, Renier and Joshua Ottens, Pieter vander Aa; the Germans Matthias Seutter and Tobias Lotter; and the Englishmen John Speed and John Ogilby.

Depending on the publisher, the maps appeared with French, Latin, Dutch, or English legends and place names. But each perpetuated Smith's (and others') nonexistent towns; faithfully reproduced the rounded and rectangular palisaded Indian villages;

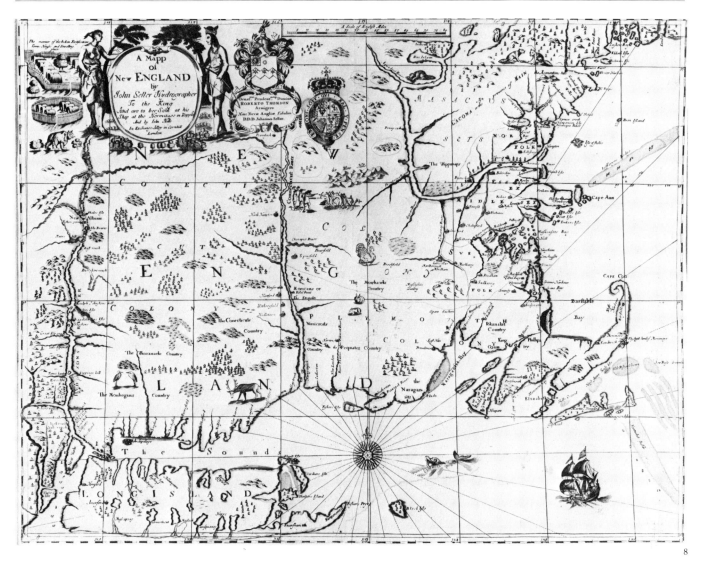

8

A Mapp of New England by John Seller Hydrographer to the King

John Seller (1627–1697)

London, 1676

Engraving with watercolor; altered state of a 1675 plate; 17¼ × 21⅝ in.

Published in Seller's *Atlas Maritimus*

Scale 1:800,000

John Carter Brown Library, Brown University

In contrast to the highly fictionalized printed works of the seventeenth and eighteenth centuries, John Seller's *Mapp of New England*, first issued in 1675, was a relatively accurate rendering of the topography and toponymy of the region. It was based on at least one, and perhaps two, now lost manuscript maps of Massachusetts that were believed to have been sent to England from Boston but that were not available to continental publishing houses. It was the first printed form of an Anglo-American type that

was to characterize New England mapping until well after the American Revolution.

John Seller, who as "Hydrographer" to Charles II and James II enjoyed a monopoloy on English mapmaking for thirty years, prepared his *New England* just following the outbreak of King Philip's War in New England. "Mounthope," "Spaw Sachem," and "King Philips Country" stand out as war-related place names; at Hadley, a group of Englishmen with muskets engage their Pocumtuck adversaries armed with bows. The original state of the plate was published in Seller's *Atlas Maritimus* in 1675 and reflects renewed English interest in New England stemming from the war; individual copies of the print were sold both by Seller and by John Hills. A later state of the plate (shown here) was issued in 1676 and included new latitudinal and longitudinal grid lines and some new elements in the bestiary. Also added was a dedication to Robert Thompson and Thompson's

arms in what was formerly a blank cartouche.

From a cartographic viewpoint, several important errors that appear on European maps of the region have been eliminated: "Iroquois Lake" (Winnipesaukee) correctly drains southward; the relative positions of the three major rivers are shown accurately; the overwhelming array of fictional town names offered by Smith, Blaeu, and others has been replaced with realistic ones. The source of these improvements was probably the London copy of a now lost map drawn in 1665 by William Reed of Boston, which had been commissioned by Massachusetts authorities to justify extensions to its northern and southern borders. (The "Indicott trees," shown in Seller's map on the southern shore of Winnipesaukee, had been planted in 1652 by Massachusetts authorities to mark the colony's northern boundaries and presumably was a key feature of the Reed map.) Other Reed-derived characteristics of the Seller map — among them the exaggerated width of the principal rivers, the shape and island-cluttered character of Winnipesaukee, and the forty-five-degree incline and snail-shell tip of Cape Cod — continued to appear on Anglo-American delineations of New England in the late seventeenth and early eighteenth centuries. Besides Seller's, these include the 1677 Foster woodcut map (9), the 1677 Stoughton-Bulkeley map (25), the 1691 Pound map (51), and the 1702 Morden map (11).

Decoratively, however, Seller was beholden to Dutch and German engravers. Seller's bestiary — fish-eating beavers, sitting beavers, standing deer, crouching rabbits, the turkey, and paired kingfishers — and round- and square-palisaded Indian villages are ectypes (or in some instances reversed images) of stock motifs in the Jansson-Visscher series (6, 7). Because Seller sometimes borrowed entire maps from the works of Dutch publishers when compiling atlases, his use of these motifs is not entirely surprising.

At least one characteristic of the Reed-derived Anglo-American "type" remained in circulation for a hundred years or more. Appearing in Cyprian Southack's *New England Coasting Pilot* from 1719 through 1733, the telltale incline and snail-shell tip of Cape Cod reappears on the Braddock Mead maps of New England from 1755 through 1777 (12, 13) and on the French ectypes of the Jefferys maps published after 1777. It even appears as late as 1783 on Abel Buell's *A New and correct Map of the United States.*

References: Stevens and Tree, 327–28; Buell; Black, *Commentary*, 63–71, 83–85; Southack; Boulind, 39–49, 61–62; BL, *Printed*, 10:473; Tooley, 574; Verner, "John Seller"; Cumming, "Charting," 84–87.

8 DETAIL

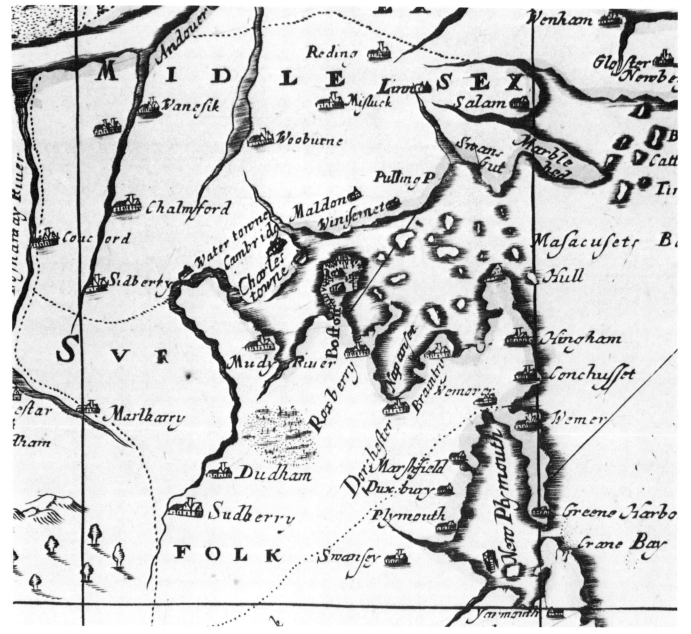

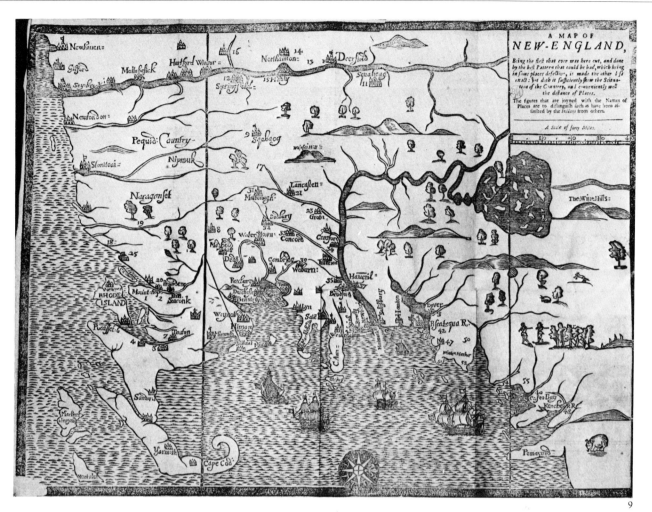

9

9

A Map of New-England

John Foster (1648–1681)

Boston and London, 1677

Woodcut, "The Wine Hills" version; 11⅞ × 15¼ in.

Published in William Hubbard's *The Present State of New-England. Being a Narrative of the Troubles with the Indians . . .*

Scale 1:850,000

Library of the Boston Athenaeum

Like all of John Foster's woodcuts, *A Map of New-England* has a primitive but attractive quality that immediately distinguishes it as an American rather than a European print. Prepared to accompany William Hubbard's history of King Philip's War, *The Present State of New England. Being a Narrative of the Troubles with the Indians in New England* (Boston, 1677), the map illustrates the extent of English settlement at the outbreak of the war and specifies by number and by name those places and communities that had been most directly involved in it. "Mount:hope,"

the site of the Wampanoag Philip's principal fort, is identified with the numeral 1.

The typeset legend in Foster's map correctly identifies it as "The first that ever was cut," all previous printed maps of the region being the work of European hands. Recent studies, however, have persuasively argued that this "Wine Hills" version of Foster's map was probably not Foster's own work but was rather the product of a London wood engraver who misread *Wine* for *White* while duplicating the print for the London edition of Hubbard's history. Indeed, a close comparison of the two woodcuts reveals that the London version was executed by a surer hand. Like John Seller's map of 1675 (8), the Foster woodcut map is cartographically related to other Anglo-American delineations of New England (11, 25, 51), which are characterized by the inclined, snail-shell treatment of Cape Cod, the exaggerated width of the principal rivers, and the clutter of islands in Lake Winnipesaukee.

At the same time, Foster's *New-England* includes features that tie it directly to the 1677 Stoughton-Bulk-

eley map (25) and presumably to the lost 1665 William Reed map on which both are based. These are the two heavy east-west lines indicating the southern and northern borders of the Massachusetts Bay Colony, which the Reed and the Stoughton-Bulkeley maps were designed to justify. (The Old Colony Line between Massachusetts and Plymouth is also shown with a heavy line.) In effect, therefore, Foster's map was a ten-year-old boundary survey that served to illustrate the location of New England towns "assaulted by the *Indians.*" As such it unintentionally revealed the ephemeral and culturally competitive nature of place names: Squakeag (Northfield), Mattabesick (Middletown), and Quaboag (Brookfield) are known on the Foster map by their Algonquian names. The Seller (1675), Hack (circa 1695), and Morden (1702) maps show these in their English forms.

References: Black, *Commentary*, 71–72; *American Printmaking*, plates 2, 3; Woodward; Deane; Holman, "Woodcut"; Boulind, 58; Tooley, 220.

10

Description of New England

William Hack (fl. 1670–1700)

London, circa 1695

Manuscript, watercolor on parchment; based on *A Mapp of New England* by John Seller, 1675; 26 × 32¼ in.

Scale 1:600,000

Pilgrim Hall

The most artistically ambitious of the surviving manuscript maps of New England that date to the seventeenth century is a parchment executed in watercolor by the London mapmaker William Hack, dedicated to Walter Yonge, an English aristocrat and Member of Parliament during the reign of William III of England. Acquired by the Pilgrim Society from an English owner in 1897, William Hack's *Description of New England in America* can be dated inferentially between 1694 and 1701, the years when Yonge served William III as a Commissioner of Customs. However, its geography and toponymy correspond so closely to John Seller's 1675

Mapp of New England (8) that it must be considered a copy of Seller's work made either as a presentation piece from Hack to Yonge or on commission from Yonge. Both Seller's and Hack's maps share the same configuration of Long Island, the foreshortening of the Maine coastline, and the treatment of Cape Ann, Boston Harbor, and the heavily stylized tributaries of the Merrimack and Connecticut rivers. Hack's 188 New England place names exactly correspond to Seller's and include Seller's duplications and errors as well as many of his spelling variants ("Salam" for Salem; "Sidbery" for Sudbury; "Linn" for Lynn). The only real toponymic innovations are thirteen place names in New York and Long Island that Hack derived from a source other than Seller, probably Robert Ryder's 1675 *Long Island*.

Hack's *Description of New England* was drawn in the decorative and technical style of a group of seventeenth-century cartographers called by map historians the Thames School after the district of London where they lived. Members of the Draper's

Company of London, the school included men such as John Daniell, Nicholas Comberford, and Andrew Welch; William Hack was among its better-known members from his habit of signing maps and because of the large number of his surviving works (331 maps and charts). He was, however, primarily a maker of manuscript atlases for presentation to royal patrons and other persons of importance. Distinguished by their use of brilliant color, stylized calligraphy, and flamboyant compass stars, the Thames School mapmakers specialized in vellum manuscript charts for navigation purposes. Their copying skill and artistic talents were appreciated by England's aristocracy and colonial administrators, who commissioned them to make working maps that might also serve to decorate walls.

References: Boulind, 1–88; Black, *Commentary*, 15–22, 84–85; Black, *Maps*, number 14, Campbell, "Draper's Company"; Phelps, 1:209; Smith, Thomas R., 83–86.

10

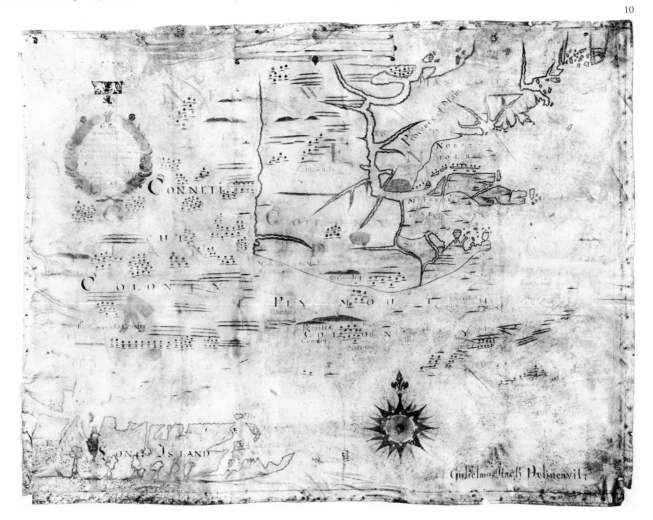

11

An Exact Mapp of New England and New York

Robert Morden (d. 1703)

London, 1702

Monochrome reproduction, with watercolor, by Old Sturbridge Village, 1953; 11⅝ × 15½ in. (sight)

Facsimile of an engraving published in Cotton Mather's *Magnalia Christi Americana*

Scale 1:1,500,000

Society for the Preservation of New England Antiquities

By the time Cotton Mather published his history of the New England ministry in 1702, geographical knowledge of New England and New York had advanced significantly from the days of King Philip's War. Long Island was now recognized as being more extended; principal rivers were perceived as much narrower. In addition, twenty or so new plantations had been founded or had assumed English names. In many other respects, however, Robert Morden's *An Exact Mapp of New England and New York*, which illustrated the towns and parishes cited in Mather's 1702 book, is a simplified eighteenth-century version of John Seller's war map of 1675 (8). "Swampfort" and "Canonicus" in the "Country of Narraganset" echo the war toponymy; "Buls," shown by Morden as a town north of Wickford, is a direct carry-over from

the Jireh Bull garrison (see 84) burned by Narragansett Indians in 1675. A number of Morden's place names are fictional: "Penicook," shown as a town with the English meetinghouse symbol, did not build its first meetinghouse until 1725. Others have gone through minor adjustments over the decades: Indicott "trees" are now a single "tree." A curious omission is the lack of stylized meetinghouse symbols for most towns in New York and Long Island. Perhaps these symbols were intended by Mather or his publishers for "proper" communities — those that supported ministers of the Puritan "Churches of Christ." Towns that supported the Church of England or Dutch-reformed churches apparently did not warrant such symbols.

Morden's *New England and New York* gained wide distribution in both England and its American colonies in the early decades of the eighteenth century. A re-engraving of this map was included as the frontispiece of the 1704 publication of *Madam Knight's Journal.* While it distorted the real borders of Rhode Island (and entirely ignored New Hampshire's existence), Morden's map, and ones like it, nevertheless remained the popularly accepted image of New England until the publication of the Braddock Mead map of 1755 (12, 13).

References: Tooley, 448; Cumming, 33; Boulind, 53; Black, *Commentary,* 82–87.

12

A Map of the most Inhabited part of New England

Braddock Mead, alias John Green (circa 1688–1757), artist

Thomas Jefferys (1720?–1771), engraver

London, 19 November 1774

Engraving with watercolor; altered state of a 1755 plate; 21¼ × 39¾ in. (top left sheet of four components)

Scale 1:300,000

Wilbur Collection, Bailey/Howe Library, University of Vermont

13

A Map of the most Inhabited part of New England (La Nouvelle Angleterre)

Braddock Mead, alias John Green (circa 1688–1757), artist

Georges Louis Le Rouge, engraver

Paris, 1777

Engraving with watercolor; 19⅞ × 19 in. (bottom right sheet of four components)

Ectype based on an engraving by Thomas Jefferys (1720?–circa 1771)

Scale 1:300,000 (inset 1:150,000)

New Hampshire Historical Society

The most detailed and informative pre-Revolutionary map of New England was drawn by the gifted London-based mapmaker Braddock Mead about 1753 and engraved and published by Thomas Jefferys in 1755. Printed on four large sheets, *A Map of the most Inhabited part of New England* was based on the general cartography of the English mapmakers John Thornton, Phillip Lea, and Robert Morden (11), but its large size allowed the delineation of town borders as well as the inclusion of numerous place names not available on any earlier map of the region in manuscript or in printed form. The Mead map was issued in four known editions by Jefferys. It was copied in reduced size by the English mapmaker John Bowles in 1765 and it was copied as a four-sheet ectype by the German Tobias Conrad Lotter in 1776 and by the Parisian Georges Louis Le Rouge in 1777. English imprints of the map were published as late as 1794, but the maps themselves were not really supplanted until the early nineteenth century in the work of the Americans Osgood Carleton, Abel Buell, and Philip Carrigain, Jr.

Important changes were made in the map between editions. Published on the eve of the 1756–1763 War for Empire between Great Britain and France, the first issue of the Mead map included an inset in the upper left-hand corner labeled "Fort Frederick, A French incroachment, built 1731 at Crown Point." The circa 1768

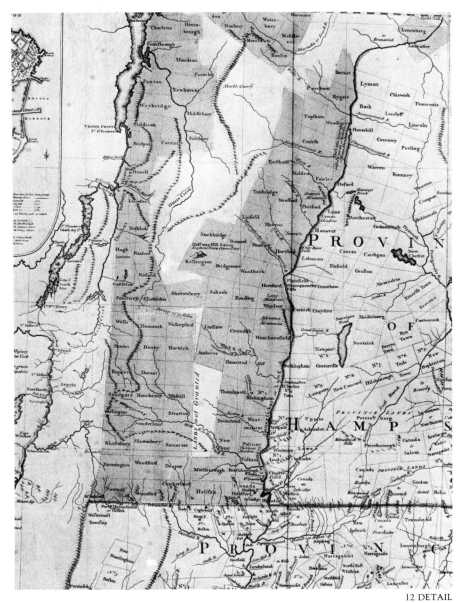

12 DETAIL

state of the upper left sheet, prepared after England assumed jurisdiction of all Canada, has the fort replaced by "A Plan of the Town of Boston," and large areas previously marked "Wilderness" are laid out and identified as townships. The 1774 issue of the two upper sheets (12) focused on an entirely different problem. In a "Note" placed below the inset, Jefferys informed his readers that the

> Connecticut River is fixed by his Majesty in Council, to be the Bounds between New York and New Hampshire.
> The Townships coloured Yellow, were granted by the Government of New Hampshire.

As French interest in the American Revolution grew, Georges Louis Le Rouge re-engraved Jefferys's 1768 issue, adapting it for French readers. *La Nouvelle Angleterre* (13), published in 1777, involved a curious blend of French and English orthography and

toponymy (for example, "Seakonnet Point et Rocks") but was cartographically a marriage of mid-eighteenth-century lower sheets and 1768 upper sheets.

Because of its detail and accuracy, the Mead map poses a problem as to its specific sources. The township jurisdictions in what are now Vermont and central New Hampshire were probably based on documents in the hands of colonial authorities in London sent by the New York and New Hampshire provincial governments who at the time were engaged in a bitter dispute over the jurisdiction of the Wentworth town grants. But where did Braddock Mead, a resident of London, obtain the names and jurisdictions of towns and counties in Massachusetts, New Hampshire, Connecticut, and Rhode Island, which in 1755 were available only in the records of the provincial assem-

blies? His source was a map twenty years in the making titled *Plan of the British Dominions of New England in North America Composed from actual surveys* prepared by the New England historian and physician Dr. William Douglass of Boston and engraved by R. W. Seale in London, 1753. This hypothesis was offered by Philip Lee Phillips in his Library of Congress list of maps on America in 1901 and was confirmed by the map scholar William P. Cumming who recently discovered that Thomas Jefferys acquired legal title to Douglass's map from his estate in 1753 and that Jefferys's 1768 edition of *A General Topography of North America* credited the Douglass engraving as the basis for *A Map of the most Inhabited part of New England* (12).

The details of Braddock Mead's life have only recently come to light. Born in Ireland about 1685, he gained a reputation for a man of "warm passions" and a fondness for "Women and Intrigue." In 1728, after abandoning two wives, he became involved with Daniel Kimberly in a scheme in Dublin in which he was secretly married to a twelve-year-old English heiress in order to obtain her fortune upon her return to England. (Clandestine marriages were capital crimes under Irish law.) Extradited to Ireland to face charges, Mead escaped and went into hiding, avoiding the fate of his partner Kimberly, who was hanged. Mead thenceforth lived and worked under the assumed names of Rogers and John Green while working as a dictionary writer and cartographer for London publishers. He ended his life by suicide in 1757.

References: Tooley, 262, 428, 170, 335; Phillips, 469–71; *DNB*, 10:706; Verner, "Fry and Jefferson"; Stevens and Tree; Boston, 43–44; BL, *Printed*, 10:475; Cumming, *Maps*, 34, 45–47; Cumming, "Charting," 93–95, 114–18, Figure 54; Chapin, *Check List*, 10; Crone, "John Green"; Crone, "Further Notes."

14

14 DETAIL

14

Massachusetts in N. Englande

Unknown draftsman

Massachusetts, circa 1633
Photographic reproduction by Henry F. Waters, 1884, 12 × 17½ in. (image) of a manuscript, ink, at the British Library, annotated by John Winthrop (1588–1649)
Scale 1:300,000

American Antiquarian Society

The earliest large-scale map of any area of New England is a manuscript now at the British Library believed to have been sent by Governor John Winthrop of Massachusetts to his friend Robert Ryece of Suffolk, England, about the year 1636. Annotated by Winthrop in the margin, the map illustrates the coastline of eastern Massachusetts and provides a superb overview of the fledgling Massachusetts Bay Colony and particularly of the relationship between English settlements and those of the remnants of Algonquian tribes still living in the area. The map is much more accurate in its depiction of coastal zones than of the interior, particularly the configurations of Plum Island, the islands of Boston Harbor, and Hull. The tidal areas are shown in detail, too: windmills, weirs, and wigwams are drawn and identified; rivers are shaded to their fall line; the roads connecting the principal English settlements from Agawam to Medford and from Dorchester to Plymouth are indicated with dotted lines.

A number of special features found on this map reappear on William Wood's map of New England of 1634 (5). These include the radical northward flow of the Musketaquid River and its island; the curious interfacing of the Musketaquid and the Charles rivers; and the depiction of Indian villages by means of three triangular wigwams, two placed above the third. It is fair to assume that these pictographic and cartographic concepts were in general circulation in the years from 1630 to 1633 or that Wood's and Winthrop's draftsmen had access to a common source map. The place names on the map (Agawam, for Ipswich; Newtowne, for Cambridge; Wessaguscus, for Weymouth) suggest a circa 1633 date; but the notes in the margin in the handwriting of John Winthrop may have been added somewhat later.

Rediscovered accidentally in the late nineteenth century in the Sloane Collection of the British Museum by the American historian and genealogist Henry F. Waters, the document is now known as the Winthrop or Waters-Winthrop map. This photograph is believed to be one of the four sent to Boston-area libraries and historical societies by Henry Waters from England in 1884.

References: Green; "Map of Eastern Massachusetts"; Seelye, 137–38; Boston, 13; BL, *Manuscript*, 3:537; Winsor, *Narrative*, 3:380–83; Boulind, 65–66; Winsor, *Kohl*, 96; Cumming, "Charting," 80–81.

15

Pascatway River in New England by I:S:

John Seller (?) (1627–1697)

London (?) circa 1660
Color reproduction by British Museum Publications, 1975, 25¼ × 37¼ in. (sight)
Facsimile of a manuscript, ink and watercolor, at the British Library
Scale 1:62,000

Richard M. Candee

A proprietary map with a purely English perspective, *Pascatway River in New England by I:S:* is one of the earliest known accurate renderings of the New Hampshire and Maine coastlines in the area of the Piscataqua

River. Dedicated to James, Duke of York, who later succeeded his brother Charles as James II of England (in 1684), the map is a brilliantly colored, stylized work that combines a cartographic plan with a perspective view. Decorative elements — symbols of houses, ships, animals, and village clusters — are drawn in a three-quarter elevation and simulate a bird's-eye perspective. The hills and mountain in the background are drawn as they might be seen on the horizon. More important than its pictography is the subtly different "position" assumed by the cartographer as he looks at his subject. In contrast to John Winthrop's map of Massachusetts Bay (14), which is "seen" from the Massachu-

15 DETAIL

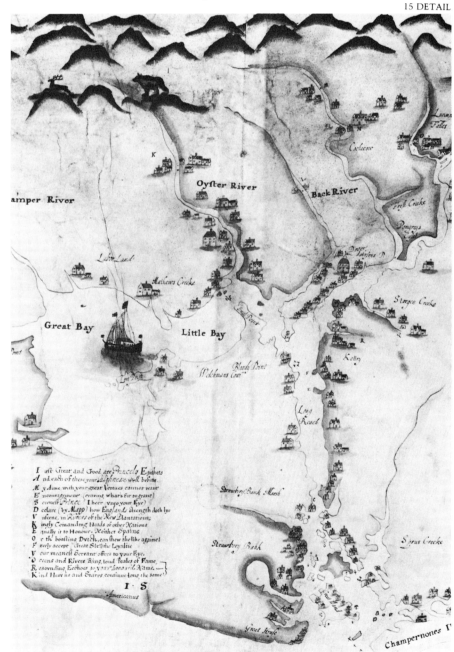

setts mainland, the I:S: map is seen by an English observer at a distance from the coastline.

Although the British Library dates this map about 1680, internal evidence suggests that it may have been drawn much earlier. The three meetinghouses shown at Exeter, Dover, and York (they are identified as buildings without chimneys and with a cupola, flagstaff, and banner) represent structures with the known respective dates of 1636, 1650, and 1652. No meetinghouses, however, are shown at Strawberry Bank (built 1657) or at Kittery (built 1659). Sawmills, identified in the key, correspond to a similar early date. If a 1660 date for this map is correct, it would correspond to the renewed interest in New England by the Stuarts after the Restoration and the return of the Duke of York from exile to serve as the First Lord of the Admiralty. Stylistically, the I:S: map has some of the elements of the Thames School of mapmakers (10), though the similarity may be more apparent than real. The most likely candidate for the identity of I:S: among the members of the Thames School is John Seller (8) who completed his apprenticeship in the Draper's Company of London in 1654. Seller is known to have successfully petitioned the Duke of York for a pardon after having been arrested and found guilty of high treason against the newly restored Stuart government in 1662. The map may have been made in gratitude for this act of clemency. The "Indian Towne Manhacok" shown in the upper left-hand corner of the map may represent an actual seventeenth-century Algonquian village.

References: Candee, "Land Surveys"; Candee, "Sawmills"; BL, Manuscript, 3:538; Tooley, 574; Verner, "John Seller"; Smith, Thomas R.

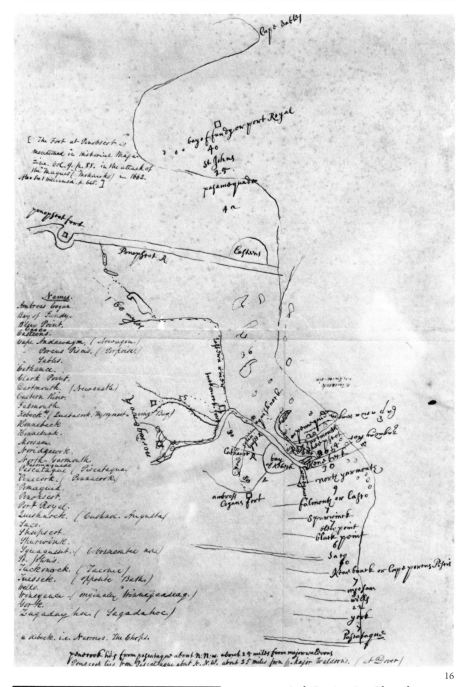

16

Mapp of the Eastern Countrey

William Pitkin (1635–1694)

New England, circa 1691

Manuscript copy, ink, by J. Hammond Trumbull, circa 1864, of a manuscript by Pitkin; 15⅜ × 10⅝ in.

Scale 1:1,000,000

Maine Historical Society

One of the essential techniques for survival in the French-and-Indian conflicts was the rapid movement of small bodies of armed men overland. The *Mapp of the Eastern Countrey*, drawn by William Pitkin when he accompanied Benjamin Church on an expedition to Maine in 1689 and 1690, is a representational map of the distances between rivers, forts, and settlements along the New England coastline from the Piscataqua River to Cape Sable. Prepared for military purposes, the map specified distances by numbers of miles rather than by relative position, presumably to allow commanders to calculate travel time between any of several key points. This technique distorted the actual topography of the coastline and interior rivers — which, for land-based soldiers, was not a critical factor. The name of each principal point, however, is clearly indicated. (The phonetic source of some of these names is revealed in Pitkin's rendering of Androscoggin as "andross Cogan.")

Born and educated in England, William Pitkin joined the Connecticut Colony in Hartford in 1659 and prepared for a career in law or in the ministry. However, he was employed in Hartford as a schoolteacher, and soon married into the Goodwin Family. At his death in 1694 he was the largest landowner on the east bank of the Connecticut River, and his will bequeathed 800 acres to his children.

In 1864 the Connecticut historian J. Hammond Trumbull made a copy of Pitkin's map (which was then in the Connecticut State Archives) and forwarded it to Edward Ballard, the Secretary of the Maine Historical Society in Portland. The original has since been lost.

References: Pitkin, xxvi–xxxi; Trumbull, J. Hammond, Correspondence; *North-Eastern.*

17

This is A true and Exact Chart or map of the Bounds and Limits of the Colony of Rhoad Island and Providence Planatations . . .

John Mumford (d. 1749)

Rhode Island, 1720

Manuscript, ink and watercolor; 23½ × 30¾ in. (in two sheets, spliced)

Scale 1:130,000

Rhode Island Historical Society

The smallest of the colonies to survive New England's 1692 jurisdictional consolidations, Rhode Island had to struggle for cartographic as well as political recognition. Most American and English maps of the seventeenth and early eighteenth centuries, among them those by John Foster (9), John Seller (8), Thomas Pound (51), and Robert Morden (11), ignored the colony's mainland boundaries and simply identified Rhode Island with Aquidneck Island and with the towns of Newport and Ports-

mouth. Providence, Warwick, and Pawtuxet — towns clearly within the bounds of the 1665 charter of Rhode Island and Providence Plantations — were relegated to Plymouth Colony, to Massachusetts Bay, or to Connecticut. Needless to say, Rhode Island's eighteenth-century neighbors made similar claims. *A true and Exact Chart or map of the Bounds and Limits of the Colony,* a manuscript survey prepared by John Mumford of Newport in 1720, was commissioned by the General Assembly of Rhode Island when it learned that the Privy Council, tired of the jurisdictional squabbling between Connecticut and Rhode Island, was planning to suspend the charters of both colonies and annex their territories to New Hampshire. An attractively colored work, Mumford's chart contrasts the original bounds granted to the colony under its 1665 charter (red lines), with the actual reduced limits of its jurisdiction in 1720 (yellow and green lines). A legend on the chart admits that the colony had agreed with Con-

17

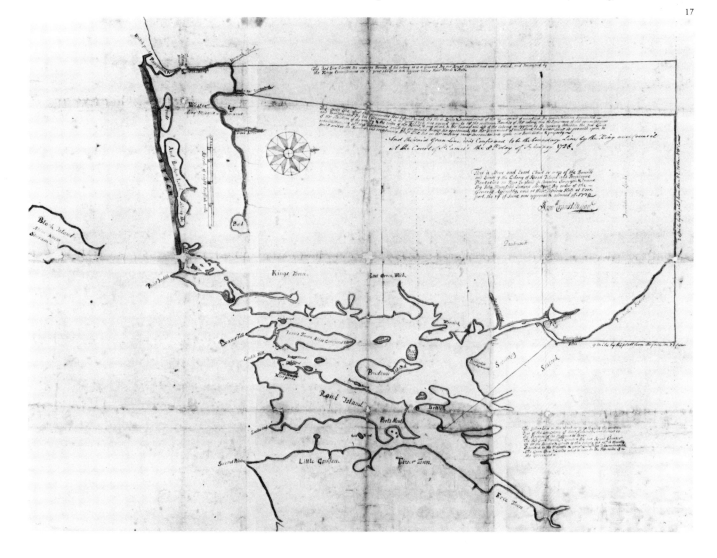

Printed for R. Baldwin in Pater Noster Row 1758

18

necticut to a compromise line in 1703 but complained that this had been done "thro the ignorance of our commissioners of the situation of the country and the corses of the Rivers." The existing boundaries between Connecticut and Rhode Island were confirmed in 1736; five years later, George II of England (who also fixed New Hampshire's bounds the same year to the disadvantage of Massachusetts) gave the Massachusetts towns of Little Compton, Tiverton, Bristol, and East Providence to Rhode Island.

The Mumford map is the earliest surviving map of Rhode Island; a manuscript copy also by John Mumford — presumably the copy passed by the Colony to the Privy Council in 1720 — is in the map collection of the Public Records Office in London.

References: Austin, 136; Van Dusen, 61; Turner, 61; Cumming, Maps, 28; Chapin, Check List, 6–7; PRO, 2:489–90.

18

A Map of the Colonies of Connecticut and Rhode Island . . .

Thomas Kitchin (1718–1784)

London, 1758
Engraving; 6¾ × 9⅛ in. (image)
Printed for R. Baldwin in Pater Noster Row for the London Magazine
Scale 1:1,000,000

Connecticut State Archives

As the eighteenth century progressed, increasing numbers of small printed maps of New England began to appear in English and later American magazines and almanacs sold and distributed to popular audiences. Thomas Kitchin, a prolific engraver and mapmaker who (like John Seller before him) held the appointment of Hydrographer to the King, engraved A Map of the Colonies of Connecticut and Rhode Island on a small plate specifically for inclusion in the London Magazine of 1758; it was the first such map to receive wide circulation.

More detailed than the Map of the British Colonies in North America, which Kitchin engraved for John Mitchell in 1755, it shows the Rhode Island–Massachusetts border after the 1741 ruling that assigned to Rhode Island the towns of Little Compton, Tiverton, Bristol, and Fagland. (Fagland is Fogland district in south Tiverton, surviving today as Fogland Point and Fogland Road.) The map also shows the Connecticut–Massachusetts border before the transfer of Enfield and Suffield to Connecticut, a move made necessary by Nathaniel Woodward and Solomon Saffery's 1642 error in measuring the southern bounds of Massachusetts Bay Colony (23).

Despite its small size, Kitchin's map shows the boundaries of many of the towns in both colonies. This again raises the question of sources. If Thomas Kitchin did not directly draw from Braddock Mead's 1755 Map of the most Inhabited part of New England (12, 13), he probably used Mead's source: Dr. William Douglass's *Plan of the British Dominions of New England in North America,* which was circulating in England as an engraved print after 1753.

References: Thompson, 30–31; *Chambers's,* s.v. "Thomas Kitchin"; Tooley, 358.

19

Eben: Smiths Map. A.D. 1780

Ebenezer Smith (1734–1807)

New Hampshire, 1780

Manuscript, ink and watercolor; 14½ × 7⅝ in.

Scale 1:700,000

New Hampshire Historical Society

Eben: Smiths Map. A.D. 1780 is a manuscript map of New Hampshire made shortly after the state declared its independence from the English Crown. The work of an untrained hand, it nevertheless contains a considerable body of topographic and toponymic detail, including county jurisdictions, town boundaries, town names, and the names and boundaries of lands set aside to repay debts incurred in the Revolutionary War, then in progress. This information was available to Ebenezer Smith, who, as a proprietor of Gilmanton, represented that town in the New Hampshire Provincial Legislature meeting at Exeter from 1775 to 1784 and who served for two years as President of the New Hampshire Senate. At the time Smith executed this drawing, the only printed maps of New Hampshire in circulation were outdated derivations of Braddock Mead's *Map of the most Inhabited part of New England* (12, 13) and a detailed, but in some instances inaccurate, map of New Hampshire and Vermont by Joseph Blanchard and Samuel Langdon published in Portsmouth in 1761. Based on proprietors' grantee maps inherited from the Wentworth administrations, as well as on the more current records of the New Hampshire Provincial Congress, the Smith manuscript was a more informed document than its predecessors, and more informed, too, than Jeremy Belknap's map, which followed in 1791. Its detail and accuracy were not surpassed until the publication of printed maps of New Hamp-shire by Samuel Holland, Samuel Lewis, Phinehas Merrill, and Philip Carrigain, Jr., which were based on individual town surveys (43).

19

References: Belknap, Jeremy, *Map;* Carrigain; Blanchard and Langdon; Lancaster, 161–62.

20

A Map of the District of Maine Drawn from the latest Surveys . . .

Osgood Carleton (1742–1816), cartographer

Amos Doolittle (1754–1832), engraver

Boston and New Haven, 1795

Engraving; 20¼ × 16⅜ in. (image)

Published in James Sullivan's *History of the District of Maine*

Scale 1:1,000,000

John Carter Brown Library, Brown University

20

Born in Nottingham, New Hampshire, Osgood Carleton pursued a military career during his early manhood. He served as a navigator and artillerist under the English flag in the second French and Indian War and under the patriot flag during the Revolution. When his health failed, Carleton founded a school for navigation, mathematics, and cartography in Boston. There he applied his training under the English Major General John Henry Bastide to the compilation of numerous maps and related publications that earned him a reputation as America's first professional mapmaker. His cartographic works included a large-format map of Massachusetts prepared under the 1794 town mapping law (published in 1798 and again in 1802); a map of Boston (1795); several maps of Maine (1795); and a map of the United States (1806). Additionally, he published a number of navigational and educational texts including the *American Pilot* (1791), the *American Navigator* (1801), the *South American Pilot* (1804), and the *Practice of Arithmetic* (1810). The Boston engraver John Norman was his colleague in his early efforts, though the latter's weak engraving skills at times proved unacceptable to Carleton's clients; Amos Doolittle of New Haven also collaborated with him.

Osgood Carleton's *Map of the District of Maine*, based in part on surveys done under the 1794 Massachusetts town mapping law, accompanied Judge James Sullivan's 1795 *History of the District of Maine*. A table of "references" notes tracts of land set aside for the "Sufferers of Portland" after the burning of Falmouth during the Revolutionary War (127). An inset map illustrates those parts of Maine District that were "harrased by the Indians." The experimental grid-townships in Washington, Hancock, and Lincoln counties were in part the basis for the vast grid of section lines that created the "checkerboard" pattern in territories west of the Ohio River.

Carleton's map was prepared before the boundaries between Maine and Quebec (represented as the "high Lands") and between Maine and New Brunswick (represented by a line drawn north of the St. Croix River) had been resolved. It was not until after the Aroostook "War" of 1844 (109) that the St. John's River was established as Maine's eastern boundary.

References: Danforth; Smith, Edgar; Tooley, 104; *Catalogue,* 191.

21

A Map of Essex County by Anna Peabody Aged 10

Anna Peabody

Essex County, Massachusetts, circa 1830

Manuscript, ink and watercolor; 9 × 10⅛ in.

Scale 1:290,000

Essex Institute

22

Connecticut

Clara B. Shattuck

New England (?) circa 1835

Manuscript, ink and watercolor; 8¾ × 10½ in. (one of a set of four)

Scale 1:500,000

Society for the Preservation of New England Antiquities

Despite a continuing need for maps and plans in settling boundary disputes and dividing undeveloped land, cartographic literacy did not make significant gains in New England until map copying became part of the secondary school curriculum in the nineteenth century as an adjunct to geography studies. *Connecticut* by Clara B. Shattuck and *A Map of Essex County by Anna Peabody Aged 10* are two examples of New England subjects drawn from a body of surviving schoolboy and schoolgirl maps produced about 1810 to 1840, many of them attractively colored and some still bound into exercise books. Clara Shattuck's *Connecticut*, a classroom copy of a printed or manuscript model, emphasizes county borders with several tints of watercolor. The principal rivers, Housatonic, Connecticut, and Thames, stand out strongly, as does a largely fictitious network of streams and tributaries (no doubt a schoolgirl's expression of *horror vacui*). Some major towns, such as Farmington, Windsor, and Saybrook, are not included, however. Anna Peabody's *Essex County*, drawn on a larger scale, is more accurate in its detail. The towns of West Newbury (incorporated 1819) and Georgetown (incorporated 1838) are not shown on the map, but this does not conclusively establish that she drew it before these dates since she may have been copying a map drawn or printed before 1819.

Little or no information has been found on either maker. The ten-year-old Anna Peabody was probably the Anna born in 1815 to Joseph and Anna Peabody of Middleton, Massachusetts. Clara B. Shattuck, however, is not listed in the Shattuck geneal-

21

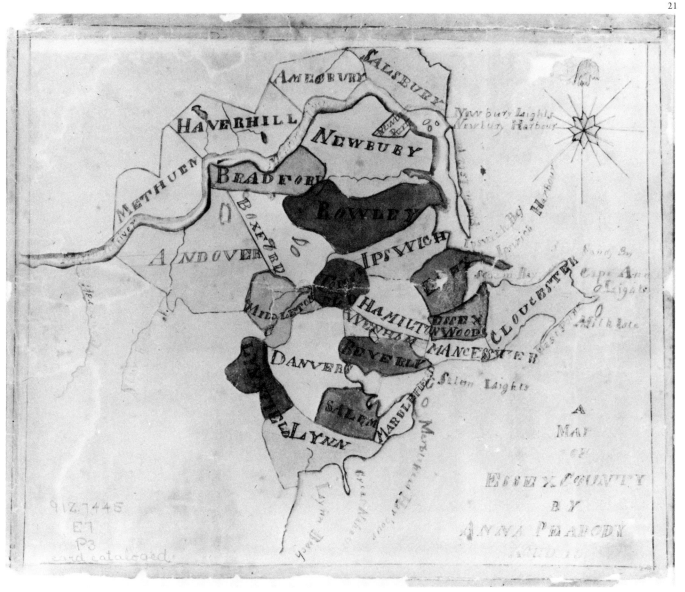

ogy. Clara Shattuck's map is among
a number of similar loose-leaf maps
of New England and worldwide geographical subjects that accompanied
a "Monitorial School book" dated
1830 and 1838, but the location of
this school has not been identified.
(Monitorial schooling involved the
teaching of younger students by older
ones.) While charmingly and naively
executed, classroom imitations of
printed sources should not be confused with vernacular maps such as
Ebenezer Smith's 1780 map of New
Hampshire (19) or Elias Frost's 1852
memory maps (74).

References: Shattuck; Peabody, 113.

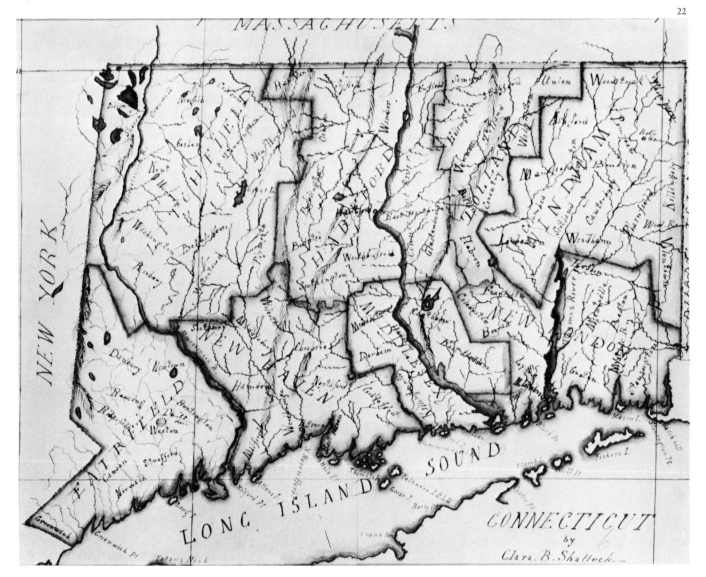

22

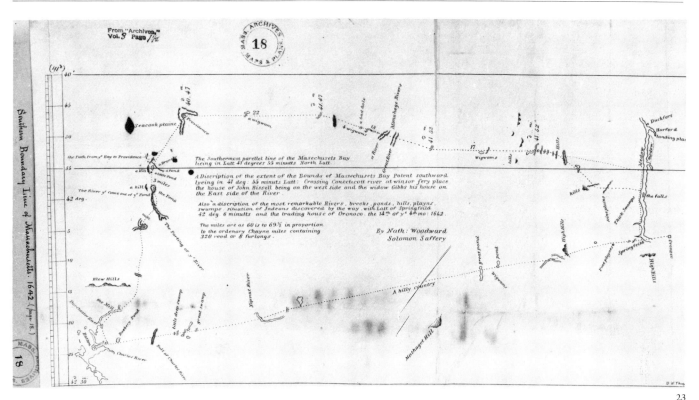

23

23

A Discription of the extent of the Bounds of Massechusets Bay Patent southward . . .

Nathaniel Woodward and Solomon Saffery, surveyors

Massachusetts, November 1642
Lithograph by B. W. Thayer, Boston, circa 1850; 9½ × 18 in.
Facsimile of an 1821 manuscript copy by A. Bradford of a manuscript by Woodward and Saffery
Scale 1:370,000

Massachusetts Archives

Not long after English settlements had been established on the Connecticut River in the 1630s, the Massachusetts Bay Colony took steps to determine the exact location of its border with the new Connecticut Colony. Accordingly, the General Court charged Nathaniel Woodward and Solomon Saffery with the task of surveying the "extent of the Bounds of Massachusetts Bay Patent southward," the first attempt to measure a colony's borders in the region's history. Titled *A Discription of the extent of the Bounds of Massechusets Bay Patent southward,* the map submitted by Woodward and Saffery on 14 April 1642 schematically represents six latitude sightings, made by the sun, along a path that began three miles below the southernmost point of the Charles River (41 degrees, 55 minutes) and ended at what was

thought to be the same latitude on the Connecticut River just north of the town of Windsor. Owing to an error, Woodward and Saffery marked the line at the Connecticut River eight miles farther south than it should have been. Later this error put the towns of Suffield and Enfield under Massachusetts jurisdiction, a difficulty not resolved until the early nineteenth century.

Of Woodward and Saffery themselves little is known. Believed to have been residents of the Massachusetts Bay Colony, they were described in the seventeenth century as "skillful and approved artizans." At least one eighteenth-century New England historian, however, termed them "obscure sailors" and "mathematicians." Many historians have attributed their eight-mile error to their sailing around Cape Cod and up the Connecticut River to arrive at Springfield and subsequently relying on hearsay (or their imagination) to describe the features that lay in between. This interpretation has been challenged by careful topographic and documentary correlation of landmarks shown on both their southern and northern routes that confirms their overland journey.

Although the original document has been lost, *A Discription* has survived as an 1821 manuscript copy made by the Massachusetts Secretary of the Commonwealth, A. Bradford; as an 1866 manuscript copy of Brad-

ford's copy by William S. Haines; and as a mid-nineteenth-century lithograph copy of the Bradford copy prepared by B. W. Thayer of Boston.

References: Bowen, Clarence, 19–20; Bradford, 2:280–81; Chase, Levi; Van Dusen, 58–59; Trumbull, Benjamin, 1:151; Ayres, 347–63; Boulind, 66–67.

24

. . . the Pequids, theire Country . . .

Unknown draftsman

Connecticut or Rhode Island, 1662
Manuscript, ink; signed by Uncas, Casasmomon, and Neesawogun; 9 × 13¾ in.
Scale 1:60,000

Massachusetts Archives

More than ten years after their successful prosecution of the Pequot War, the United Colonies of New England passed a resolution disallowing the conquered Pequots to be a distinct people or "to retayne the name of Pequatts, or to settle in the Pequatt country." Nevertheless, by 1660 enough remnants of this decimated Algonquian nation were still alive that authorities in Massachusetts and Connecticut, who jointly administered Pequot affairs through Indian intermediaries, were accusing one another of failing to set aside reserved lands that would keep the Pequots in check. *The Pequids, theire Country* represents a schematic map made in 1662 of a ten-mile section of the coastline of present-day Rhode Island just east of the Pawcatuck River. An affidavit attested to by spokesmen of three Indian tribes most directly involved, the map was solicited by agents of the Massachusetts Colony in an attempt to define the former eastern bounds of the Pequot nation, as "a brooke called weepcodawa," and a "water or pond called nekeequow-eese." If accurate, it fixed the eastern bounds in present-day Charlestown, Rhode Island. The affidavit was signed by Uncas, chief of the Mohegans; by Casasmomon (or "Robin"), a Pequot administrator; and by Neesawogun, a Narragansett. The colonies agreed upon a reserved tract for the Pequots in 1667.

While this is an English document, it shows a characteristic Indian reliance on place names rather than on measured points of reference. For example, "the pond called teapanocke" by the Narragansetts is "called by them [the Pequots] mupquota." This same characteristic is seen in the language of the 1666 King Philip map (78), which lists "the principal names of the land" that Philip was willing to sell to the English. Present-day Rhode Island place names that can be recognized on this document include Weekapaug and Pawcatuck; fragments of names include Quonochontaug Pond and Misquamicut.

The Indians' recollection of these Pequot bounds may have been mistaken or even deliberately misleading. According to Roger Williams's "rude view, how the Pequots lie" (sent to Governor John Endecott and John Winthrop in 1636), the Pequot nation extended between the Thames and Mystic rivers. Territories to the east of the Mystic and the Pawcatuck were occupied by the eastern Niantics and the Narragansetts.

References: Bradford, 2:257–58; Vaughan, 176–84; Thompson, 24; Williams.

25

[Boundaries of Massachusetts Bay Colony]
William Stoughton (1632–1701) and Peter Bulkeley (1643–1688)

Massachusetts, circa 1677
Color reproduction, number 8 in *The Blathwayt Atlas,* published by Brown University Press, 1970; 23 × 28 in.
Facsimile of a manuscript "exactly Copied about 1678 from an Original lent S.r Robert Southwell by M.r Stoughton and M.r Buckley"
Scale 1:500,000

John Carter Brown Library, Brown University

The restoration of Charles II to the English throne in 1660 and the subsequent hardening of England's policy toward its foremost Puritan colony in America generated a number of maps commissioned by the Massachusetts Bay Colony designed to explain or justify that colony's claims against the territories of neighboring New Hampshire. At the heart of its claim was the clause in the 1628 charter of the Massachusetts Bay Company that defined the colony's territory as

All that parte of New England in America . . . betweene a great River . . . called Monomack alias Merriemack and a certen other River there called Charles River . . . And also all those landes . . . which lye and be within a space of three English Myles to the Northward of the saide River called Monomack alias Merrymack . . .

Not long after the charter was signed, explorers discovered that the Merrimack River turned north a few miles inland rather than continuing due west. In 1652 a Massachusetts expedition to Lake Winnipesaukee fixed the outlet of this lake as the northernmost point of the river, and on this basis claimed the entirety of the Mason patent and an important segment of the Gorges patent in Maine and New Hampshire.

The first map justifying this claim was prepared in 1655 by William Reed of Boston under a contract from the Massachusetts General Court, which had been ordered to produce such a map by a Royal commission charged with investigating conditions in the New England colonies. Because the vessel bearing the Reed map to England was intercepted by a Dutch

24

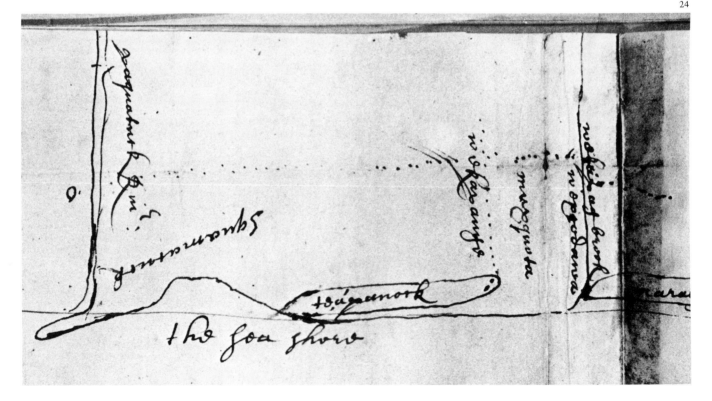

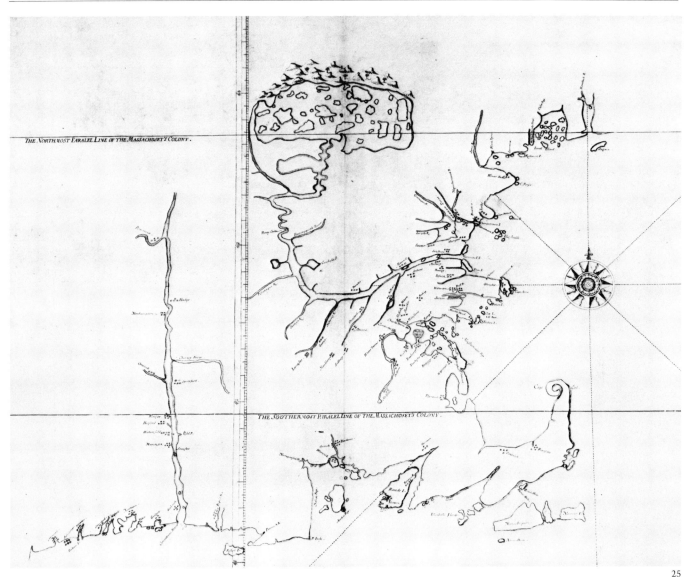

THE NORTHMOST PARALEL LINE OF THE MASSACHOSETS COLONY.

THE SOUTHERMOST PARALEL LINE OF THE MASSACHOSETS COLONY.

25

privateer, the document failed to reach its destination. After ten years of delay, the Massachusetts General Court contracted with the surveyor James Taylor of Reading to produce another such map, presumably based on the file copy of the Reed map, to give to its agents William Stoughton of Dorchester and Peter Bulkeley of Concord who were sent to answer a summons from the Lords of Trade and Plantation in London.

The Stoughton-Bulkeley map of 1677, more accurately the map "exactly Copied about 1678 from an Original lent [to]S.ᵗ Robert Southwell by M.ʳ Stoughton and M.ʳ Buckley" is believed to be a copy of the Taylor map (which has also been lost) that William Stoughton and Peter Bulkeley brought with them to England. Part of an atlas assembled by William Blathwayt in the seventeenth century to assist the Lords in administering England's colonial holdings, the copy

is executed in a fine secretarial style. It has been described as "the first official map of Massachusetts and the first locally made map of New England"; but it has also been characterized as a misleading document that deliberately foreshortened the northern reach of the Merrimack in order to make Massachusetts's claim appear reasonable. Like the 1675 Seller map (8) and the 1677 Foster map (9), which may also have derived from the Reed-Taylor surveys, the Stoughton-Bulkeley map bears the telltale characteristics of seventeenth-century Anglo-American maps of New England: the snail-shell configuration of Cape Cod and the inclination of the Cape's southern shoreline. Two heavy lines mark the "Northmost" and "Southermost" boundaries of the Massachusetts Colony. A prominent latitude scale intersects the map at its center.

References: Tuttle; Black, *Maps,* number 8; Black, *Commentary,* 63–71; Wheeler, 64–66; Tooley, 531; Cumming, "Charting," 86.

25 DETAIL

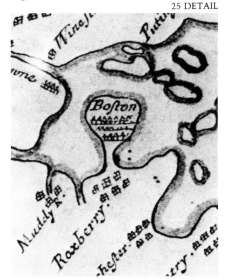

26

A Map of the Towns of Hattfield, Hadley &c

Unknown draftsman

Massachusetts, 1709
Manuscript, ink; 14 × 22 in.
Scale 1:50,000

Massachusetts Archives

Because of their fertile alluvial soil, intervale lands along the flood plains of the Connecticut River were the frequent source of disputes between Englishmen and Indians and between Englishmen and Englishmen. A sketch map drawn to illustrate the boundaries of the several towns involved, *A Map of the Towns of Hattfield, Hadley &c* was prepared in the course of a continuing struggle for control between these two towns over intervale lands on the west (Hatfield's) side of the "The Grt. River Connecticott." The lands in question (shown on the map as the Great Ponset and Little Ponset meadows) abutted the Hatfield Rivulet (present-day Mill River) where it joined the Connecticut River. These meadows had in part been granted to Hadley by the Colony Court and in part been purchased by Hadley from Northampton; in an early Hadley lot division, they were termed "west side" lands. They included a tract called "Indian Bottom" or "Indian Hollow," which was the original planting ground used by the Pocumtucks and others but abandoned after 1660. In its petition to the General Court to assume jurisdiction over all lands on the west side of the river, Hatfield pointed out that Hadley had not prevented Hatfield from assuming the cost of providing public services (ministry and schooling). In a letter to Hadley, Hatfield also pointed out that unless the "Great River" were made the boundary between them, the town of Northampton would probably gain Little Ponset. Begun in 1709, the controversy was not settled until 1733 when the General Court made the river the boundary between the towns.

The characteristic layout of Connecticut Valley towns on a long principal street parallel to the river is pointedly revealed by the terms "Hadley Street" and "Hattfd Street" and in the north-south alignments of each as shown in the sketch.

References: Mass. Archives, Hadley; Judd, 29–30; Wells and Wells, 127–28; Massachusetts, *Acts*, 9:92, 129.

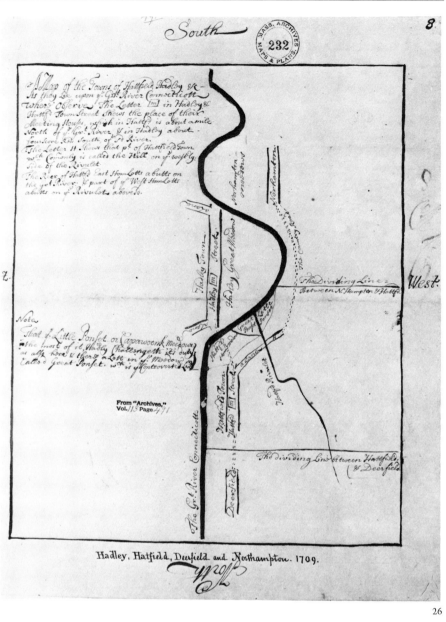

Hadley, Hatfield, Deerfield and Northampton. 1709.

26

27

[Mason's Curve Line]

Unknown draftsman

New Hampshire, mid-eighteenth century
Manuscript, ink; 16½ × 13⅜ in.
Scale 1:400,000

New Hampshire Historical Society

When Sir Ferdinando Gorges and John Mason dissolved the Laconia Company in 1624, the Piscataqua River was chosen as the dividing point between their respective holdings. As proprietor of the New Hampshire tract, John Mason assumed all rights south of the Piscataqua within a radius of sixty miles from the mouth of this river. When Mason died unexpectedly in 1632, neither his immediate family nor his descendants drew

any benefits from this grant, which was never legally replaced or abrogated. After considerable litigation, however, a great-great-grandson of Mason sold what was left of these rights to a group of ambitious Portsmouth merchants and provincial magistrates in 1746. Under the name "Masonian Proprietors," this group realized significant profits by reselling legal title to unoccupied tracts within the sixty-mile limit.

The difficulty of fixing the exact bounds of Mason's holdings is illustrated by a survey taken of the western arc of the "Curve Line," probably commissioned by the Masonian Proprietors shortly after 1746. Beginning at "The tree Three miles North of pantucket Falls" (the point at which the province line between Massachusetts and New Hampshire headed due west), the surveyors marked "abeach" (beech) on the Province Line sixty miles inland from the Piscataqua and continued in a northeast arc for sixty-seven miles. Each five-mile interval was marked on a nearby tree ("Hemlock - Black oak - Beach - Beach - Wild pair . . .") and a new compass bearing was begun three and a half degrees more easterly than the previous setting. The principal ponds and lakes intersected by the line include Center Pond, Ashuelot Pond, Sand Pond, Long Pond, Lake Sunapee, Little Sunapee, and Newfound Lake. The task of measuring the line was not completed in the eighteenth century. Carrigain's *Map of New Hampshire* of 1816 notes that the portion running between Wilmot and the Merrimack was "imaginary as that portion of it was not surveyed." Mason's curve line can be recognized today as the western boundary of the towns of Fitzwilliam, Marlborough, Stoddard, Washington, and Wilmot.

References: Carrigain; Blanchard and Langdon.

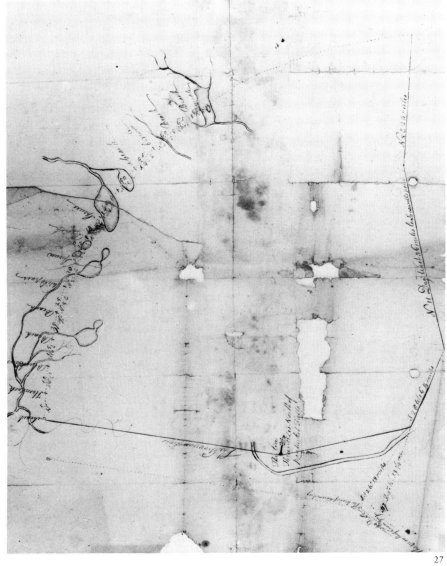

27

28

A Small Map of the Sea Coast of New England Together with the Out Lines of Several of the Provinces lying thereon.

Unknown draftsman

England, 1738
Engraving, with manuscript additions; 13⅜ × 22⅞ in.
Scale 1:2,000,000
New Hampshire Historical Society

Boundary disputes among the four New England colonies were so common in the eighteenth century that English mapmakers printed outline maps of the principal boundary reference points in the region and the dates and presumed limits of the individual colony and province grants. *A Small Map of the Sea Coast of New England Together with the Out Lines of Several of the Provinces lying thereon* summarizes New England

boundaries as they existed in 1738 and allows anyone unfamiliar with the American colonies to understand and grasp the boundary situation at a single glance.

It is one of the first printed confirmations of Rhode Island's mainland jurisdiction, most other maps of the period restricting the colony to Aquidneck Island. New Hampshire is shown bound by Mason's curve reaching "60 Miles Deep into the Country." Gorges's portion of Maine (lying between the "Nywickwannock" and "Kennebeck" rivers) and all the Maine and Nova Scotia tracts lying to the east of the Kennebec and St. Croix rivers are shown belonging to the Province of Massachusetts. Plymouth, described as the "Late Colony," is also within the Massachusetts bounds. A manuscript notation on the verso side of the backing of this map states that it was sent from England to Governor John

Wentworth and received by him in Portsmouth in 1773. While the circumstances cannot now be confirmed, he may have requested this map to help him explain to dissatisfied members of this council why the 1765 decision to put the Wentworth grants on the west bank of the Connecticut River under New York's jurisdiction was in keeping with historically established colonial policy.

References: BL, *Manuscript*, 3:536; Phillips, 469.

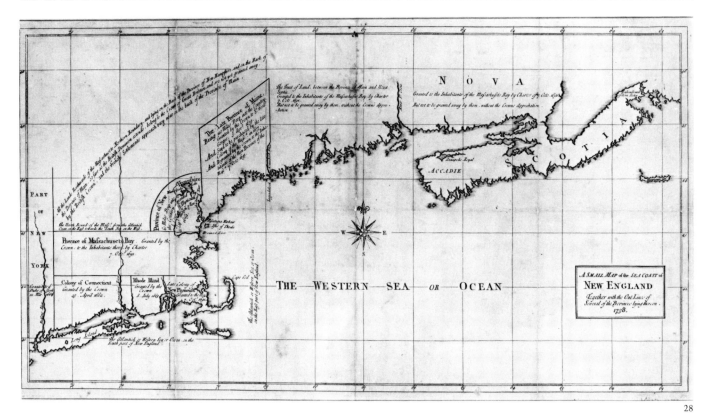

28

29

[Merrimack and Piscataqua Rivers]

Unknown draftsman

Massachusetts, circa 1726
Manuscript, ink; 15 × 19 in.
Scale 1:300,000

Essex Institute

30

Plan

Unknown draftsman

New Hampshire, circa 1750
Manuscript with wash and watercolor; 19
  × 15⅜ in.
Scale 1:300,000

New Hampshire Historical Society

One of the most far-reaching consequences of England's decision in 1628 to set the boundary of the Massachusetts Bay patent "three English Myles to the Northward of the . . . Merrymack" was the controversies between separate groups of proprietors who had been awarded the same land by different governments. Penacook township, later known as Rumford (and still later as Concord, New Hampshire), was originally granted by Massachusetts in 1725 to a group of proprietors residing in Andover. In 1727, however, New Hampshire granted a tract of land named Bow, eighty-one square miles in size, located on both sides of the Merrimack River and including most of Pena-

cook; it also granted three more new towns (Epsom, Chichester, and Canterbury) that were more than three miles distant from the river. The Bow proprietors included virtually all the politically prominent people in New Hampshire in 1727; the Governor, Lieutenant Governor, the Governor's Council, and members of the Assembly. When the 1740 border settlement (31) placed Penacook (by then Rumford) under New Hampshire jurisdiction, the Bow proprietors (who had made no attempt to develop their grant) initiated a trial lawsuit against John Merrill, a Rumford ferryman, in an attempt to coerce compensation from the Andover settlers. In a series of self-serving decisions, the New Hampshire courts awarded the case to the Bow interests, setting off a struggle that pitted political privilege against the legitimate rights of the residents of Rumford and that was not resolved until after the intercession of George III in 1762 to nullify the decisions of the New Hampshire courts. A subsequent agreement reached in 1771 provided that the Bow proprietors be reimbursed a token ten pounds for each one-hundred-acre lot of the original grant.

The untitled pen-and-ink map of the Merrimack and Piscataqua rivers (29) and the watercolor-and-ink *Plan* (30) illustrate the beginning and end of the Rumford-Bow controversy. The first was prepared after Rumford, Pen-

acook, and Suncook were granted by Massachusetts authorities in January 1725 and before New Hampshire authorities granted the townships of Hopkinton, Gilmantown, and Canterbury in 1727. Its presumed purposes were to indicate the Penacook and Suncook grants (shown by dotted lines) and probably to demonstrate that they lay south of the boundary claimed by Massachusetts. The map can therefore be said to have been drawn from a point of view sympathetic to Massachusetts. At the same time, like maps relating to Algonquian affairs (24, 77, 78), the document relies on names rather than on measured distances. Beginning with the "Burying Place" (located at some point close to "Endecott Trees" on the seventeenth-century printed maps), the map identifies fifteen tributaries of the Merrimack by their Algonquian names, placing the two new townships between the Contoocook and Suncook rivers.

The *Plan*, on the other hand, was prepared some time after the border decision of 1740 when the New Hampshire courts were settling the question of whether the Bow or the Rumford proprietors legally owned the area granted to them in 1725 and 1727. The plan identifies the boundary claims of Massachusetts in the seventeenth and early eighteenth centuries as well as the boundary after the 1740 adjudication. It illustrates the location of the Massachu-setts-granted townships of Suncook and Rumford and the four townships, including Bow, granted by the New Hampshire government in 1727. Bow is shown with a double line. Since the *Plan* identifies the Bow proprietors as "Respondents," it was prepared on behalf of the Rumford interests as plaintiffs. It may be a copy of a 1753 plan that accompanied the Rumford minister Timothy Walker and his fellow townsman Benjamin Rolfe to England when they sought action with the King in Council to reverse the decisions of the New Hampshire court. Three manuscript plans showing the disputed boundaries of Suncook, Rumford, and Bow are in the map collection of the British Library.

References: Lyford, 1:37, passim; Bouton, 205–13; BL, *Manuscript*, 3:538.

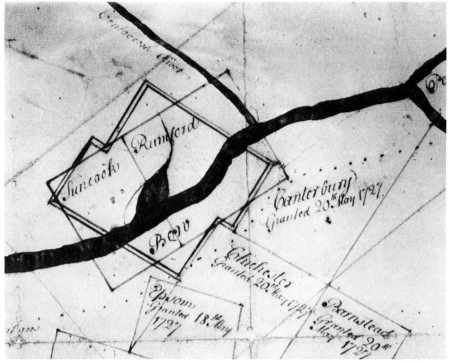

30 DETAIL

29

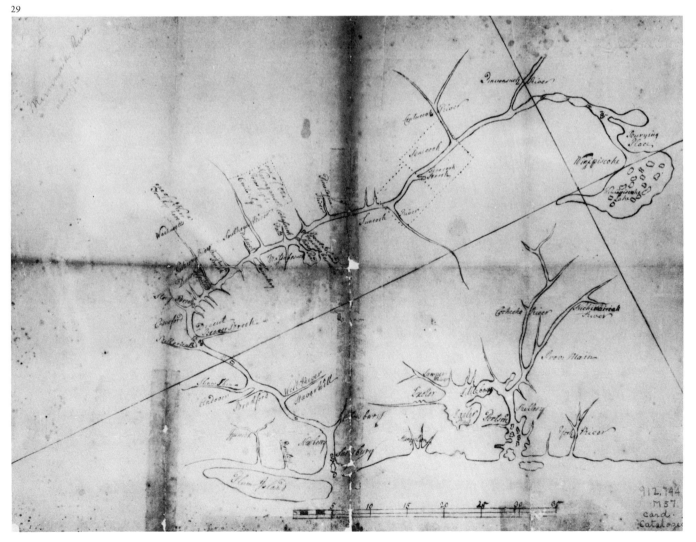

33

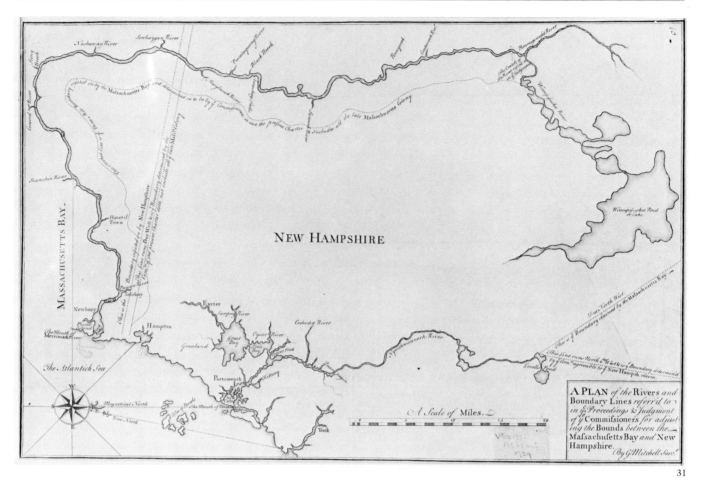

31

31

A Plan of the Rivers and Boundary Lines . . .

George Mitchell, surveyor
W. H. Toms in Union Court, Holborn, engraver
London, 1739
Engraving; 12⅝ in. × 18 in.
Scale 1:200,000
New Hampshire Historical Society

In 1737 and again in 1739 the American surveyor George Mitchell prepared a plan of coastal New Hampshire and the Merrimack River to accompany reports submitted by Commissioners who were attempting to settle the border dispute between New Hampshire and Massachusetts. *A Plan of the Rivers and Boundary Lines referr'd to in yᵉ Proceedings & Judgment of yᵉ Commissioners for adjusting the Bounds between the Massachusetts Bay and New Hampshire*, engraved in London in 1739, illustrates the alternate boundaries claimed by New Hampshire and by Massachusetts, as well as the recommendations of the Commissioners. Massachusetts claimed all territory below a line drawn three miles "north" of the Merrimack to a point near the "Crotch" at the junction of the "Pemmigewaset" and "Winnipissiokee" rivers. By contrast, New Hampshire claimed all lands above an east-west line three miles north of the center of the Merrimack at its mouth. The Commissioners, chosen among representatives of neighboring colonies and provinces, in turn recommended a similar east-west line approximately one mile north of the one proposed by New Hampshire. In the end, Massachusetts was penalized for its territorial ambitions. The line chosen by George II on 5 March 1740 conformed to the Massachusetts solution only so long as the Merrimack headed in a southerly direction. At the point the river headed north (Pentucket or Pawtucket Falls), the line went due westward, thereby cutting off approximately twenty-eight Massachusetts towns and giving them to New Hampshire.

Little is known of George Mitchell except for brief mention of his name by the eighteenth-century historians William Douglass and Jeremy Belknap in their descriptions of the Commissioners' attempt to adjust the Massachusetts–New Hampshire boundary. The English map scholar R. V. Tooley credits Mitchell with a 1750 map of the Island of Canso and Cape Sable.

References: PRO, 2:2558–62; Belknap, Jeremy, *History*, 1:237–57; Tooley, 441; Douglass, 1:423.

32

... the Boundary Line between the Commonwealth of Massachusetts and the State of Newhampshire . . .

Caleb Butler (1776–1854)

Massachusetts, August 1825 (Groton)
Manuscript tracing, ink and watercolor, made in 1863 of manuscript by Butler; 18⅞ × 28⅜ in.

Scale 1:40,000

New Hampshire Historical Society

In 1825 the states of Massachusetts and New Hampshire agreed to rerun their boundary line, which had been measured under the provincial governors Jonathan Belcher and Benning Wentworth in 1741. Accordingly, three commissioners from each state accompanied the surveyor Caleb Butler and a crew of chainmen to measure the thirty-five-mile segment of boundary between the Atlantic Ocean and a point three miles north of Pentucket Falls, and the fifty-six-mile segment running due west from this point to the Connecticut River. Reference points such as stones, heaps of stones, gravel pits, logs, and stumps were marked and recorded. Copies of the survey were put on deposit in their respective archives. *The Boundary Line between the Commonwealth of Massachusetts and the State of Newhampshire*, an 1863 manuscript copy of Butler's 1825 plan, records the easterly portion of the survey where the boundary adjoined the towns of Salisbury and Amesbury in Massachusetts and Seabrook and Southampton in New Hampshire.

The difficulty of running a line "parallel" to the uneven course of the river is revealed in the decision taken by surveyors in 1741 and in 1825 to run the line between the ocean and Pentucket Falls in twenty straight courses, each point being fixed three miles north of the center of the river. (The first nine of these courses are shown on this portion of Butler's map.) A historian, mapmaker, lawyer, and land surveyor, Caleb Butler was a native of Pelham, New Hampshire, and a graduate of Dartmouth College. He was a resident of Groton, Massachusetts, and author of an 1852 history of that town.

References: Appleton's, 1:478; BL, *Manuscript*, 538; PRO, 2:2501.

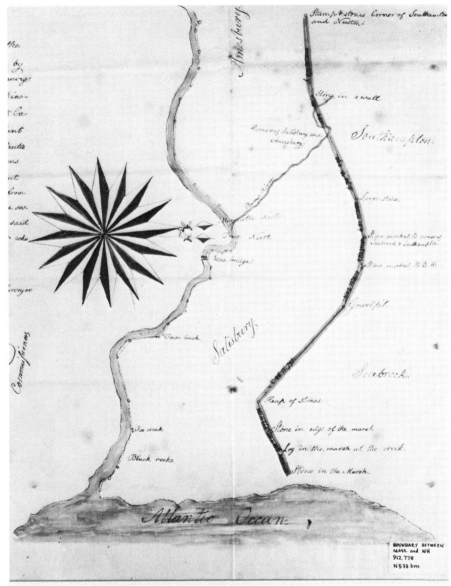

32

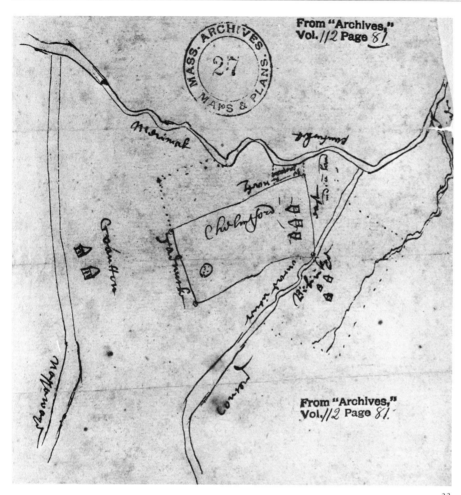

From "Archives,"
Vol. //2 Page 81

From "Archives,"
Vol. //2 Page 81.

33

---

ran a survey of the town for the 1831 Massachusetts town mapping law, the "India[n] Land" had become the City of Lowell.

References: Massachusetts, *Records*, 1:319; Waters, Wilson, 2–5; French; Hales.

34

. . . Towneship of Squnshapag . . .

Joshua Fisher (circa 1610–1672)
Massachusetts, April 1667 (Mendon area)
Manuscript, ink; 15⅜ × 11¼ in.
Scale 1:63,000
Massachusetts Archives

Less than ten years separated the founding of Chelmsford in 1653 and a petition (made in 1660) by a group of Braintree proprietors for a plantation at "Netmocke" adjoining the Dedham grant. During those intervening years, however, the planners of Puritan villages in New England had raised their sights from six miles square to "eight miles square" and were granting lots on the basis of wealth: 150 acres of land were to be allotted at Netmocke for each one hundred pounds of estate owned by a settling family. Netmocke had changed its name to Squanshapaug, and by 1667 a sufficient number of families had been attracted to the plantation to allow the Braintree proprietors to apply for the privileges of a township.

Joshua Fisher's *Towneship of Squnshapag* accompanied the petition of the inhabitants for a confirmation of the eight-mile-square grant of land purchased from John Anawassanauke and William Quashaaniit (?) of "Bleue Hills." Occupying portions of six present-day Massachusetts towns (Hopedale, Mendon, Blackstone, Bellingham, Franklin, and Wrentham) and two present-day Rhode Island towns (Woonsocket and Cumberland), the grant abutted the Dedham grant on the north and "Country land" on the east, south, and west. The survey overstepped by at least one mile the legal southern limits of the Massachusetts Bay Colony (three miles below the southernmost reach of the Charles River). The plantation gained recognition as the town of Mendon on 15 May 1667 but was abandoned and entirely destroyed in the first year of King Philip's War.

Joshua Fisher's role as surveyor reveals the special position that professional surveyors held in a society where the most available commodity of wealth was land. A member of the

---

33

Chelmsford

John Sherman (?)
Massachusetts, 1656
Manuscript, ink; 6 × 6 in.
Scale 1:200,000
Massachusetts Archives

In 1641 the General Court of the Massachusetts Bay Colony enacted a law requiring that every new town within its jurisdiction have its bounds surveyed and recorded within a year after its grant had been made. The first of several town mapping laws passed by the Massachusetts legislature, the act was in keeping with the interests of a colony whose history was characterized by territorial control and expansion. (By way of contrast, Rhode Island enacted no mapping laws at any point in its history.) One of the earliest towns to comply with this law was Chelmsford, which prepared a map in 1656, now in the Massachusetts Archives.

As originally projected by its proprietors in 1653, Chelmsford was to encompass "six myles Square of upland and meadow . . . at the meri-

---

macke River at a necke of land nere to Concord river." When it was laid out, however, the town formed a rectangle approximately seven by four miles in area, located in an offset angle to the Merrimack, and without river frontage. In 1656 the town successfully petitioned the General Court for a northerly extension of its grant so that its bounds would abut a section of the Merrimack. *Chelmsford*, which may have been drawn by Captain John Sherman of Watertown, who made the original survey of the town, accompanied the town's petition for an extension. Groton is shown on the west; Billerica, on the east; "India[n] Land" (probably desirable land under cultivation) is indicated in a pie-shaped section between Chelmsford's east bounds and the Concord River. One hundred thirty-eight years later when Frederic French ran a survey of Chelmsford bounds for the 1794 Massachusetts town mapping law, the "India[n] Land" was within the town's jurisdiction and was occupied by five sawmills, two grist mills, a fulling mill, an iron works and trip hammer, a canal, and three bridges. Thirty-seven years after this when John G. Hales

Dedham Church in 1639, Joshua Fisher was a Representative to the General Court and served Dedham as town clerk for four years, from 1657 to 1661; he served as a Dedham selectman for twenty-one years, one of three men who virtually monopolized the town's affairs during the seventeeth century. His inventory, taken in 1672, indicates that he was also an inn holder and an officer in the local militia. In his position of trust and authority, he was appointed to fix the bounds between Dedham and Dorchester in 1655. Besides the Squanshapaug survey, he was responsible for nine other surveys in the Massachusetts Archives (see 81) dated between 1651 and 1672; this work took him as far as Deerfield on the Connecticut River.

References: Lockridge, 187–92; Metcalf, 2–13; Smith, Frank, 166; Mass. Archives, Fisher; Fisher; Jenney.

35
Bounds of the town of weare
Joseph Baker

New Hampshire, 1749

Manuscript copy, ink, made after 1764 of a manuscript by Baker; 11⅞ × 13¾ in.

Scale 1:35,000

New Hampshire Historical Society

The *Bounds of the town of weare* is a land division plan, probably a clerk's copy of an earlier document by Captain Joseph Baker of Pembroke, New Hampshire, assigning 100- and 120-acre rights to the Robiestown proprietors following a lottery in 1749. "Beverly Canada," as the town of Weare was first known, was surveyed in 1735 by the Province of Massachusetts for the ostensible purpose of reimbursing with land grants the heirs of soldiers from Beverly, Massachusetts, who had taken part in

34

Phips's expedition to Canada in 1690, but for the real purpose of legitimizing Massachusetts sovereignty over the western side of the Merrimack (31). Because a principal beneficiary of this grant was Colonel Robert Hale, of Beverly, the tract was sometimes called "Halestown" or the "township of Hale" and is so cited in Middlesex County deeds. When the 1740 border settlement put the tract under New Hampshire jurisdiction, the Masonian Proprietors successfully challenged the Massachusetts grantees and in 1749 negotiated its sale to a group of proprietors from Hampton Falls led by Meshech Weare and Ichabod Robie. As a result, the tract lost its Massachusetts orientation and was known alternately as "Col. Weare's Town," or "Robiestown." (By contrast, the Canada grant to Ipswich, which also fell to New Hampshire jurisdiction but which was not challenged by the Masonian Proprietors, retained its Massachusetts name, "New Ipswich.") Weare acquired its present name at its incorporation in 1764 when Meshech Weare was a rising and successful justice and important member of the New Hampshire General Court.

The lot divisions and range ways recorded in the *Bounds of the town of weare* were as impermanent as the tract's early names. According to the terms of the 1749 lottery, rights were arranged into seven principal east-west ranges, each subdivided into four sections. Between each range and each section was an allowance of two-rod or four-rod rights-of-way for building roads. Set aside in the approximate center of the tract (between the fourth and fifth ranges) was "The Center Square," which was to "contain six acres, and be left . . . for a meeting house." The actual placement of roads, farmsteads, and meetinghouses, however, followed an entirely different pattern. The first major road was cut in a direction "most Sutable from the way that goes by Amuskiege up to the Center Square"; the town's meetinghouse was built in lot 55 of the first range, approximately three miles south of "Center Square."

References: Little, William 286–95; Kneeland.

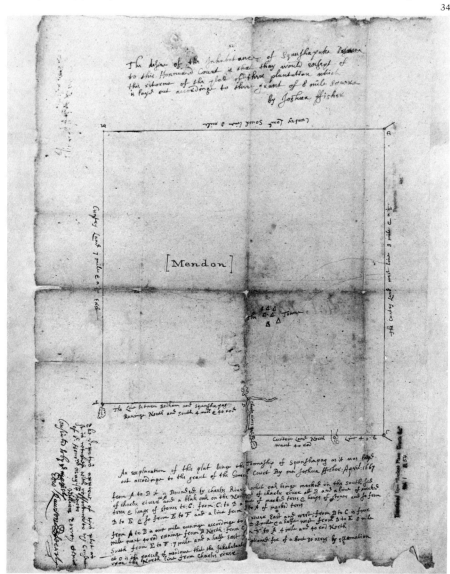

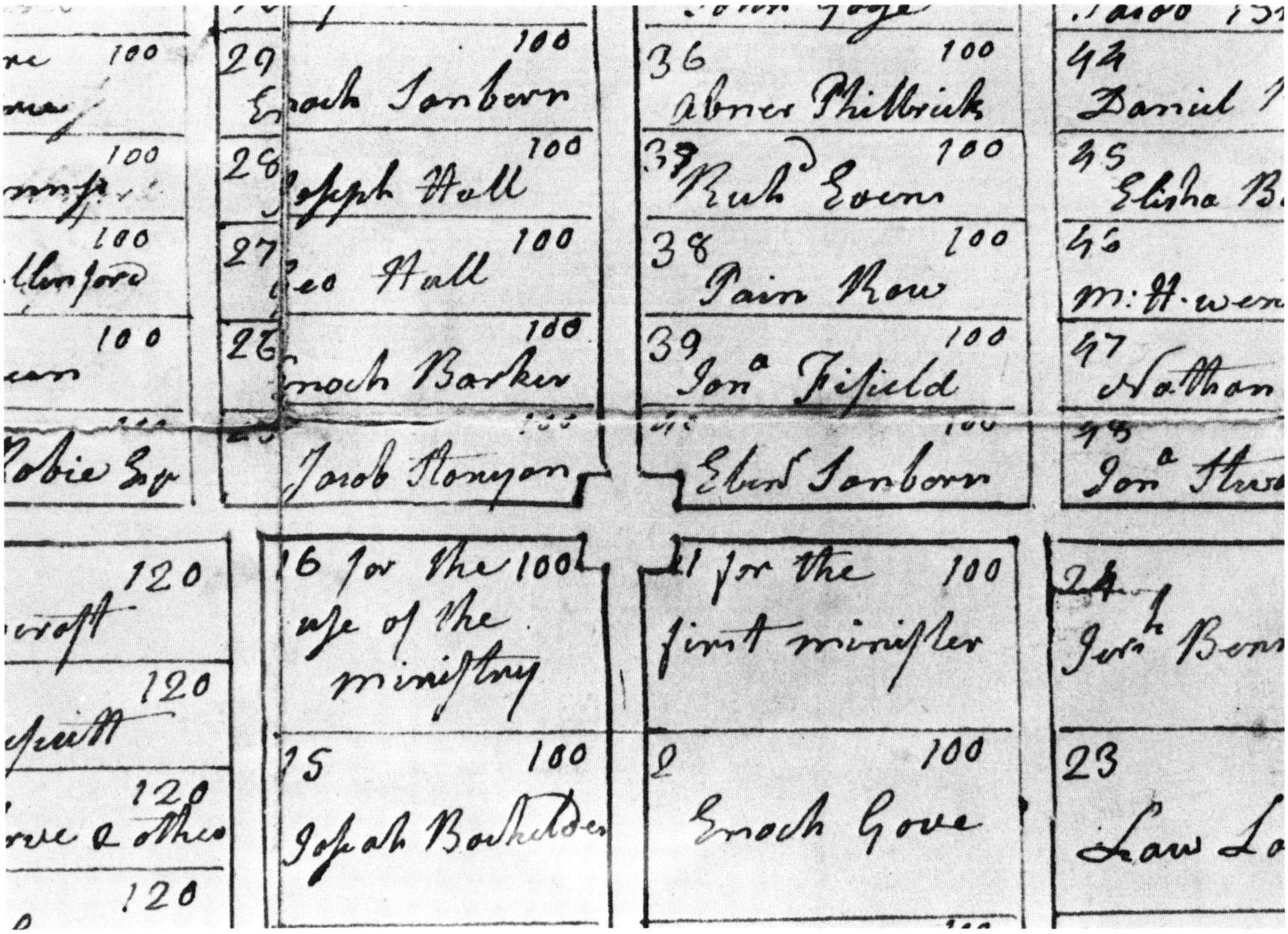

100	29 Enoch Sanborn 100	36 Abner Philbrick 100	44 Daniel ?
100	28 Joseph Hall 100	37 Rich'd Evens 100	45 Elisha B.
100	27 Geo Hall 100	38 Pain Row 100	46 M: H. wen
100	26 Enoch Barker 100	39 Jon'a Fifield 100	47 Nathan
Robie Esq	Jacob Stonyon	Eben'z Sanborn	Jon'a Stee
120	16 for the use of the ministry 100	11 for the first minister 100	24 Jos'a Ben
120			
120	15 100 Josiah Batchelder	2 100 Enoch Gove	23 Law Lo
120			

35 DETAIL

36 *

[Haverhill, Massachusetts]

Unknown draftsman

Haverhill, Mass., after 1769
Manuscript, ink; 14¾ × 18¾ in.
Scale 1:41,000

Essex Institute

Haverhill, Massachusetts, located on the north bank of the Merrimack River, was one of several towns split in half by the 1740 New Hampshire–Massachusetts boundary decision (31). At some later point in the eighteenth century, the town commissioned a survey to ensure that its boundaries with the newly formed towns of Plaistow and Atkinson, New Hampshire, were accurately laid out. Beginning with the "Brandy Arow" station on the east, the survey located the four other principal stations fixed by the surveying team that ran the New Hampshire–Massachusetts border in 1741 and noted the locations of approximate bench marks for future reference.

Untitled and undated, the resulting plan was drawn after the 1765–1769 completion of the Baptist meetinghouse in Haverhill (seen as the smaller of the two meetinghouses at the village center) and after Atkinson built a meetinghouse in 1769. The plan was unusual in one important respect: the surveying team took sightings from three promontories to locate specific points in Haverhill in their relation to meetinghouse spires in several adjoining towns. Sightings were taken from "Ayers Hill," a "Hill back of round Pond," and a high point on the road to Atkinson. The distance at which these sightings were made (approximately twelve miles to "Rowley House"; fifteen miles "to Ipswich"; and ten miles to "Andover S. Meetg. House") suggests that the surveyors were using an improved theodolite, a telescopic instrument developed by the Englishman Jonathan Sisson in the early eighteenth century that provided accurate inclination and angle measurements.

References: Chase, George, 584–86, map 16; Morse, 24–25; Richeson, 145–50.

37

Louden, October 30 1794

Joab Griswold

Massachusetts, 1794

Manuscript, ink and watercolor; 20 × 19 in.

Scale 1:40,000

Massachusetts Archives

In 1794 Joab Griswold, "Surveyor of Lands for Hartford County" (Connecticut), was hired to survey the boundaries of the town of Louden, Massachusetts. He was probably chosen for this because his work was familiar to some of the first settlers of the town, who originated from Hartford County. Griswold's *Louden, October 30 1794* was drawn to the specified scale of two hundred rods to an inch and encompassed what later

became the eastern half of the town of Otis. The plan is a typical sample of many surveys submitted by Massachusetts towns to comply with the Commonwealth's 1794 mapping law. Six sawmills are shown, each illustrated by a schematic mill building; three principal county roads; and a number of ponds and streams. Appropriately, the strongest visual aspect of his plan is the town's borders, shown in thick black lines. The principal east-west road in Louden — the main axis around which early homesteads and settlements aggregated — was a military road laid out by General Jeffrey Amherst and his army in 1759 while on a march from Boston to Albany. Called "the great road from Boston to Albany," it was later the line of march of Burgoyne's captured army, and several British deserters settled there. Three thousand acres or

approximately twenty-three percent of the town's land area lay under the water of nine ponds. This stimulated the growth of mills, but inhibited the agricultural development of the town.

The pictographic style employed by Griswold in the Louden survey matches the styles he used in the division of Simsbury lands in 1786 (88). This includes the use of distinctive pine trees; houses whose opposite gable ends are seen simultaneously; and the use of cross-hatching to indicate roofs.

References: Holland, 2:540–43.

37

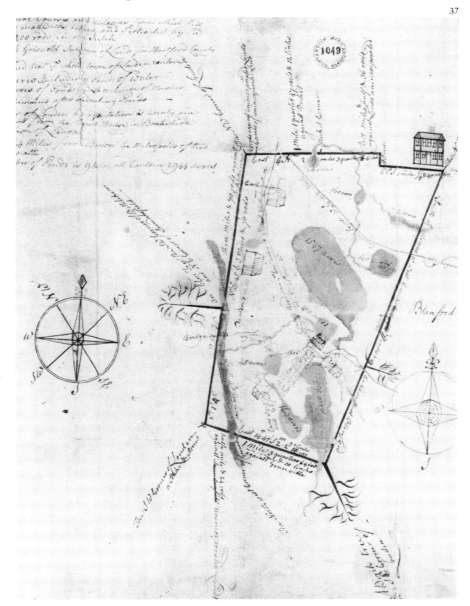

38*

A Plan of the Town of Sherburn . . .

Unknown draftsman

Massachusetts, 26 June 1794

Manuscript, ink, signed by five selectmen of Sherborn; 12⅞ × 18½ in. (image)

Scale 1:40,000

Massachusetts Archives

One of the most unusual maps in the 1794 town series in the Massachusetts Archives is *A Plan of the Town of Sherburn* prepared by an unidentified surveyor working under the town's selectmen. Rather than placing the compass rose in a discreet corner of the plan, the surveyor drew the entire plan *within* the compass, the only known example like this. The design was probably artistic in purpose; the draftsman also framed the map and course calculations in yellow watercolor borders. The effect, however, simulates a globe or "world" and underscores the autonomy and inward vision of New England towns in the eighteenth century. At the center of the "world" of Sherborn is the meetinghouse, the point from which local authority emanated in the eighteenth century. At the outer periphery are the courses, landmarks, and bodies of water that distinguish familiar territory from the "terra incognita" of Natick, Dover, Medway, Holliston, and Framingham.

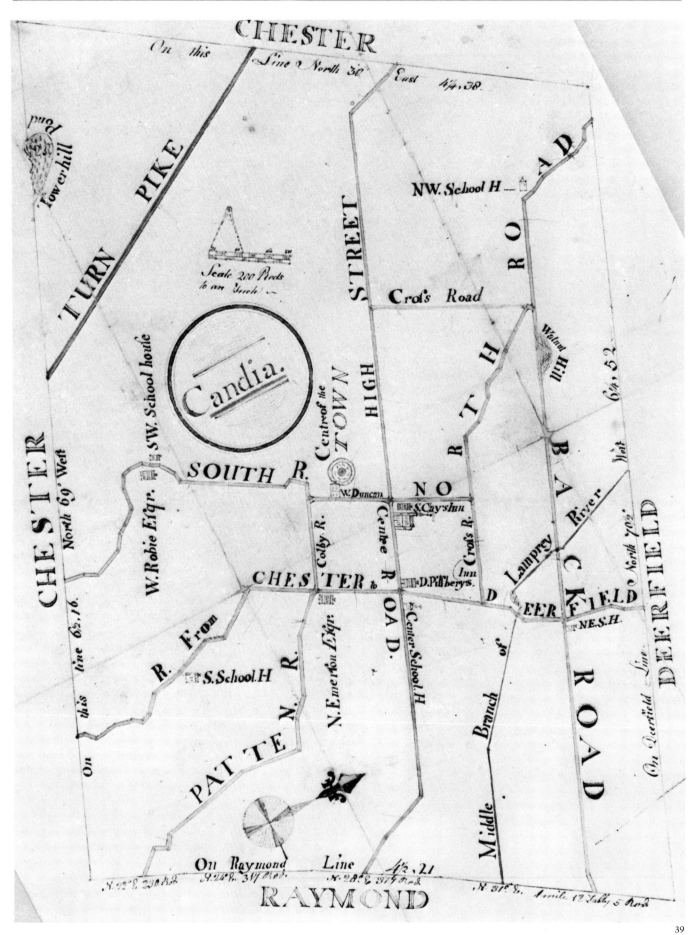

39

An Accurate Map of the Town

Richard Emerson (1721–1824)

New Hampshire, 1805 (Candia)
Manuscript, ink; 15⅝ × 10¾ in. (sight)
Scale 1:40,000

New Hampshire State Library

40*

Plan of Deerfield 1805

Unknown draftsman

New Hampshire, 1805
Manuscript, ink; 19⅛ × 14½ in. (sight)
Scale 1:40,000

New Hampshire State Library

Richard Emerson's *An Accurate Map of the Town*, dated 1805, was commissioned by the selectmen of Candia to comply with New Hampshire's 1803 mapping law (43). Illustrating a town approximately forty years after its settlement, Emerson's map has a number of pictorial elements that echo the style of his contemporary Phinehas Merrill (44–49), a New Hampshire mapmaker active from 1790 to 1810. These elements include the use of the bull's-eye symbol to indicate the "Centre of the Town"; the use of capitals in the names of principal roads; the lettering style and positioning of the names of contiguous towns; and the capricious mixing of Latin, Gothic, and italic lettering in the legend. At least one architectural feature confirms the regional identity of the map. The meetinghouse has an outside stairwell porch on the gable side opposite the steeple, a practice commonly followed in southern New Hampshire and in eastern Massachusetts but entirely absent on the Connecticut coastline. The locations of the town's five schoolhouses suggest that a majority of residences were situated in the eastern and southern portions of the town. However, unlike those in Weare (35), at least two principal roads in Candia were originally laid out as range ways in the "second part of the Second Division" of land rights in the town of Chester shortly after 1719. These are the Back Road to the point where it reaches the Northwest School House; High Street and Center Road; and several smaller roads that intersect transversely with these two.

Richard Emerson, the son of Col. Nathaniel Emerson of Candia, was the grandson of Samuel Emerson of Chester. The grandfather, an original settler of the town of Chester, was responsible for laying out the proprietors' shares in the second part of the

Second Division and probably the eighty-acre lots in the Third Division.

Also drafted for the 1803 New Hampshire mapping law, the *Plan of Deerfield 1805* outlines a much more complex shape than Candia's. In part this shape reflects several parcels of land on Deerfield's boundary with Nottingham (its parent town), whose owners were politically strong enough to remain in Nottingham rather than be included in the Deerfield separation of 1766. But in most other ways the town conforms to the orderly pattern that characterized steady growth. Like Candia's, the meetinghouse at Deerfield is within a few hundred feet of the town's exact geographical center. A network of roads follows the geometric range system under which proprietors' rights were divided. (One road is named "Six Range Road.") The town's population (cited by Belknap as 1,619 inhabitants in 1790) supported a proportionately larger number of inns (eleven) but maintained only two schoolhouses. The Deerfield meetinghouse is a twin-porch structure with exterior stairwells located at each gable end, a regionally distinct type that is common in the Massachusetts and New Hampshire uplands. Later, when the town had the money, one of these porches was converted into a bell tower.

References: Moore, 496; Eaton, 77; Bell, Charles, 38; Belknap, Jeremy, 3:226.

41*

A Correct Plan of Plainfield taken from the survey of Abel Knap in 1793

John Johnson (1771–1842)

Vermont, circa 1793
Manuscript, ink and watercolor; 17¼ × 21⅝ in.
Scale 1:20,000

Wilbur Collection, Bailey/Howe Library, University of Vermont

42

A Map of Albany

A. Johnson

Vermont, 1818
Manuscript, ink and watercolor; 7½ × 9½ in.
Scale 1:130,000

Wilbur Collection, Bailey/Howe Library, University of Vermont

---

Like the *Bounds* of Weare, New Hampshire (35), *A Correct Plan of Plainfield* and *A Map of Albany* are examples of lot division plans made at a time when proprietary land development in New England had been refined to a smoothly working routine, but also when available land was virtually exhausted. Prepared on behalf of the proprietors of range towns located in central and northern Vermont, these plans, or copies of them, were submitted for routine approval to the state legislature.

A Correct Plan of Plainfield taken from the survey of Abel Knap in 1793 illustrates the town after one or two years of settlement. The exact ranges have been broken up or consolidated as proprietors exchanged, sold, or transferred their rights to settlers or to other proprietors. At least one road actually follows a plotted range way (a rarity); several lots have been reserved for public use. Both Abel Knap (who made the original 1793 survey) and John Johnson (who redrew the "correct" version of the plan) were prominent in the early history of Plainfield and the State of Vermont. A former resident of Rehoboth, Massachusetts, Abel Knap served as a judge of probate and was elected Plainfield town clerk and town representative for forty-eight and fourteen years, respectively. In this regard he followed a pattern found in seventeenth-century Dedham (34). John Johnson, a professional surveyor living in Burlington, served as Surveyor General of Vermont for many years and was one of the commissioners supervising the adjudication of the American-Canadian border in 1817.

A Map of Albany, drawn in 1818, shows the division of land before settlement: a geometric grid superimposed on a six-mile-square area regardless of topography. Some lots are almost wholly under water; others are mountainous. One of the last plans prepared for a New England town, *A Map of Albany* illustrates land speculation in its pure state without the cultural encumbrances of a colonial, Puritan society. Lots are laid out without regard for religion (church lots, meetinghouse squares, and parsonage lots) or for political benefactors and, indeed, without the usual lots reserved for schools. "A. Johnson" has not been identified.

References: Hayward, 20, 66–67, 99–100; Hemenway, 1:596–99, 3:47–70, 4:713–34.

42

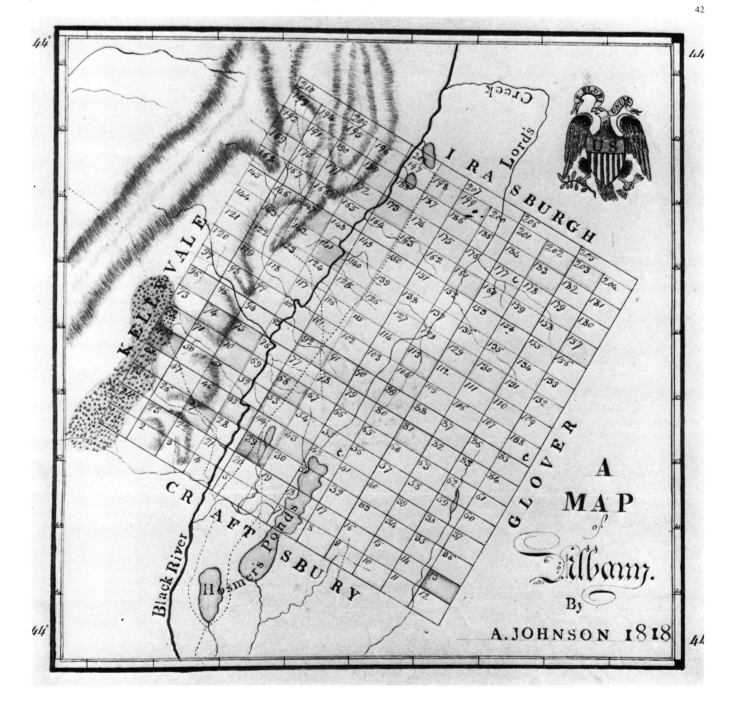

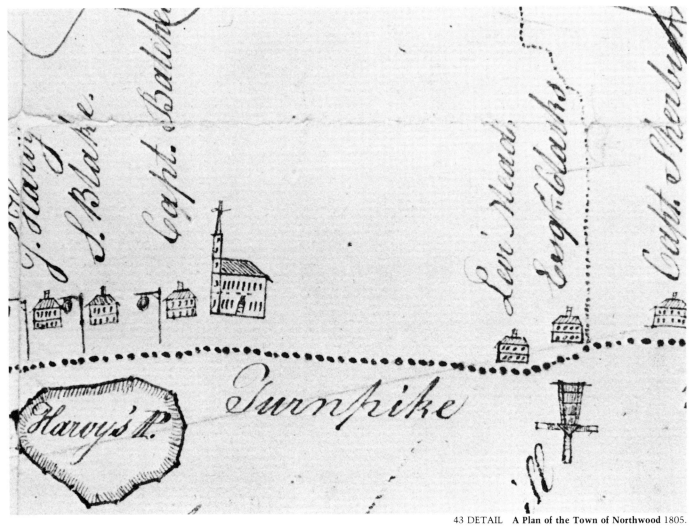

43 DETAIL   **A Plan of the Town of Northwood** 1805.

43

Bound Folio of 1803 Series Town Maps

New Hampshire, 1803–1806

Volume 3, Moultonborough to Woodstock; 28 × 42 in. (open), D. 3 in.

New Hampshire State Library

Following the system devised by Osgood Carleton (20) for the State of Massachusetts in 1794, New Hampshire in 1803 ordered every town in its jurisdiction to survey its boundaries for the purpose of compiling and publishing an accurate map of the state. The task of unifying these surveys into a single map was given to Philip Carrigain, Jr., New Hampshire's Secretary of State, and to Phinehas Merrill (44–49), a mathematician and schoolteacher in Stratham. The initial legislation was titled *An Act to Cause the Several Towns, Parishes, and Places within this State to be Surveyed for the Purpose of Obtaining a Map of this State.* It was approved 30 December 1803 and required that each town submit a measured plan of its boundaries

> together with a description of all public roads passing through the same, also the rivers, falls, and principal streams, ponds, lakes and mountains, . . . the whole to be protracted by a Scale of 200 rods to an inch.

A fine of $150 was to be incurred by any town neglecting to submit a survey by the first Wednesday of November 1805.

The project was beset with delays. In June of 1806, the New Hampshire General Court instructed Carrigain and Merrill to return any surveys that lacked sufficient detail and extended the submission date to 1806. In 1807 the Court gave Carrigain and Merrill a three-year extension to complete the project and additionally gave Carrigain a loan of $5,000 to be repaid in three years. In 1810 Carrigain and Merrill were given a second extension to 1812; this extension was renewed three times. Finally in 1816 the General Court voted to file suit against "Carrigain and others" for the recovery of the note — an action apparently made unnecessary by Carrigain's delivery to the legislature of 250 copies (half the number contracted for) on 25 December 1816, for which he was reimbursed $3,750. Drawn to a scale of 800 rods to an inch, the map was distributed to the selectmen of each town and later to each incorporated academy in the state. It was known as "Carrigain's 1816 Map" and was the first published map of the state based on measured boundaries. The folio volume included in the exhibition is one of three presently in the collections of the New Hampshire State Library into which the originals of the 1803 series have been bound with silk interleaving.

44

Plan of the Town of Stratham

Phinehas Merrill (1767–1815)

New Hampshire, 17 July 1793
Engraving; 10 × 7⅞ in.
Scale 1:40,000

New Hampshire Historical Society

45

Plan of the Town of Stratham

Phinehas Merrill (1767–1815)

New Hampshire, 17 May 1806
Engraving, altered state of a 1793 plate;
9¾ × 7¾ in. (sight)
Scale 1:40,000

New Hampshire State Library

46

A Plan of the Compact Part of the Town of Exeter . . .

Phinehas Merrill (1767–1815), artist
A. M. Peasley, engraver

New Hampshire, 1802
Engraving; 5 × 12½ in. (sight)
Scale 1:3,000

Society for the Preservation of New England Antiquities

47 *

Copperplate for **A Plan of the Compact Part of the Town of Exeter**

Phinehas Merrill (1767–1815), artist
A. M. Peasley, engraver

New Hampshire, 1802
Copper sheet; 15 × 12½ in. (image)

Exeter Public Library

48 *

A Plan of the Town of Portsmouth Including New-castle, or Great-island:

Phinehas Merrill (1767–1815)

New Hampshire, 1805
Manuscript, ink and watercolor; 11 × 14½ in.
Scale 1:40,000

New Hampshire State Library

49

Plan of the Town of New-Castle with the adjacent Islands

Phinehas Merrill (1767–1815)

New Hampshire, 1806
Manuscript, ink and gray wash; 6½ × 8½ in. (sight)
Scale 1:40,000

New Hampshire State Library

Born in Stratham, New Hampshire, in 1767, Phinehas Merrill was a self-taught civil engineer and surveyor who produced a number of medium- and large-scale maps of towns in the Piscataqua region. Merrill was also an author, penman, and schoolteacher of local repute who either taught or influenced surveyors and mapmakers active in surrounding towns (see 39). Serving his community at various times as a selectman, town clerk, town representative, and school committeeman, he also compiled materials for a gazetteer of New Hampshire published in 1817 by his brother Eliphalet Merrill, a Baptist minister and revivalist in neighboring Northwood. Together with Philip Carrigain, Jr., New Hampshire's Secretary of State from 1805 to 1808, Phinehas Merrill coordinated and compiled the 1803 series of New Hampshire town

maps for the purpose of producing Carrigain's 1816 *Map of New Hampshire*, the first map of the state based on measured surveys (43). Phinehas Merrill's publishing ventures included a printed map of Stratham (1793) and two printed maps of Exeter (1802), which were engraved by A.M. Peasley. Merrill also wrote and published the *Scholar's Guide to Arithmetic*, which came out in four editions between 1793 and 1802, and prepared plans of Greenland, Barrington, Portsmouth, New Castle, and Rye, all dated 1805 and 1806. Phinehas Merrill died in 1815 at the age of forty-eight before he had a chance to complete the map project with Carrigain or the gazetteer with his brother. Among the surveying instruments cited in his inventory were a spirit level, a compass, a chain, a scale and dividers, a "large semi circle,"

44

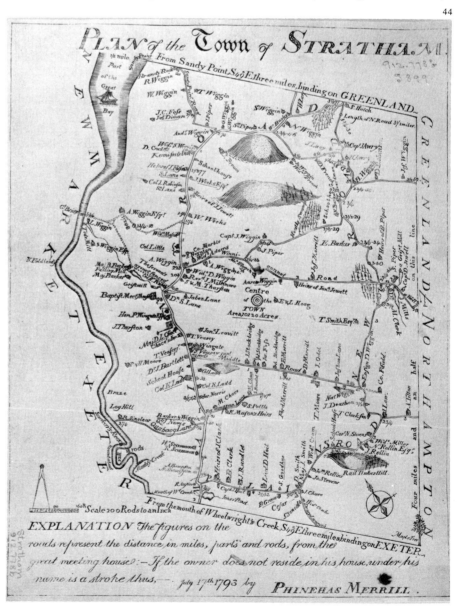

and a Gunter's scale. He owned pews in both the Congregational meetinghouse ($15.50) and the Baptist meetinghouse ($15.50) and left a farm and buildings in Stratham and a farm and buildings in nearby Bow. He was survived by his wife Phebe and two daughters.

One of Phinehas Merrill's earliest maps was *Plan of the Town of Stratham*, a print first issued 17 July 1793 and reissued in an altered state in 1806 to comply with the New Hampshire 1803 mapping law. Drawn to a scale of 200 rods to an inch, this map plots the locations and owners' names of approximately 150 dwelling houses in Stratham in 1793 and 1806. The numerals and fractions shown at intervals on the roads indicate the distance in miles, fractions of miles, and rods from the "great" (Congregational) meetinghouse as measured

by road travel. Trees are rendered by horizontal lines of decreasing width; the bull's-eye symbol marks the "Centre of the TOWN"; and hill symbols are shown in profile or elevation accompanied by hatching and stippling. Despite their naive characteristics, Merrill's two versions of *Stratham* are sophisticated demographic and cartographic documents. They revealed that almost half the population of Stratham lived on the "MAIN ROAD" that led from Exeter to Portsmouth (the present New Hampshire State Highway 101). On or adjacent to this road were the Congregational and Baptist meetinghouses, two schoolhouses, two inns, a fulling and grist mill, and the residences of most of the town's leading citizens, including a minister, judge, two physicians, and five militia officers. (The names of absentee own-

ers are underlined.) More important, no fewer than fifty-six erasures or substitutions represent changes taking place in the decade between the first and later states, including Phinehas Merrill's own acquisition of Major D. L. Chace's homestead directly beside the Congregational meetinghouse. These involve nine transfers of ownership between individuals with the same surname; nineteen transfers between individuals with different surnames; three new houses; three new roads; the relocation of one schoolhouse; and the conversion of one private home into a tavern. Perhaps the most startling change is the erasure of thirteen names and houses (including a small house formerly owned by "Cesar," a common name for northern blacks), which represents a loss of about one house per year. While fires may account for some of these, a majority may have been the result of abandonment and subsequent decay after the incapacity or death of the owner. If Merrill's data are accurate, there was a net loss of ten dwelling houses in Stratham at a time when its population remained at approximately 900 inhabitants.

Merrill's *A Plan of the Compact Part of the Town of Exeter*, a print issued under his and engraver Peasley's names in 1802, was a companion to a smaller-scale map titled *A Plan of the Town of Exeter* issued by Merrill and Peasley the same year. Illustrating what was then the second-largest maritime and manufacturing town in New Hampshire, the *Plan of the Compact Part* specifies not only the location but the structural and architectural features of individual buildings and bridges. On Court Street, for example, can be distinguished the fifth meetinghouse of the First Parish in Exeter, completed only two years before Merrill published this map and still standing today. Hipped roof structures — such as Judge Tenny's residence, the Court House, Academy buildings, and the residence of T. Smith, Esqr. — can be differentiated from gable-ended structures, and single-chimney residences from twin-chimney. A cross-baluster fence and colonnaded trees line the road to the Academy. As the "Head of the Tide" on the Exeter River (the fall point above which coastal shipping could not pass), the town was the natural focus of numerous early industrial manufactories. No fewer than eight mills, a nail factory, and a post office are concentrated alongside the banks of the lower falls basin and

45

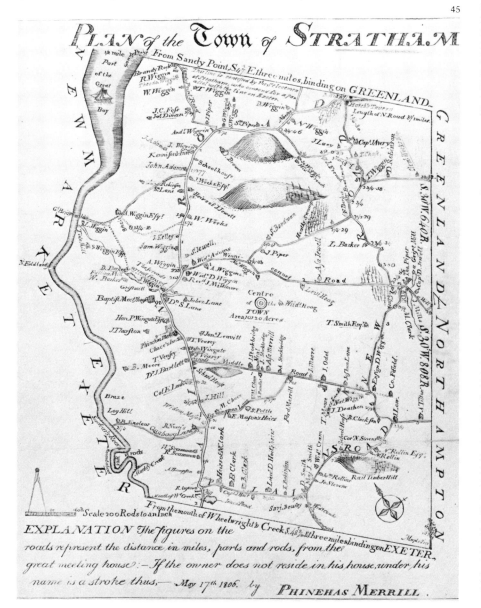

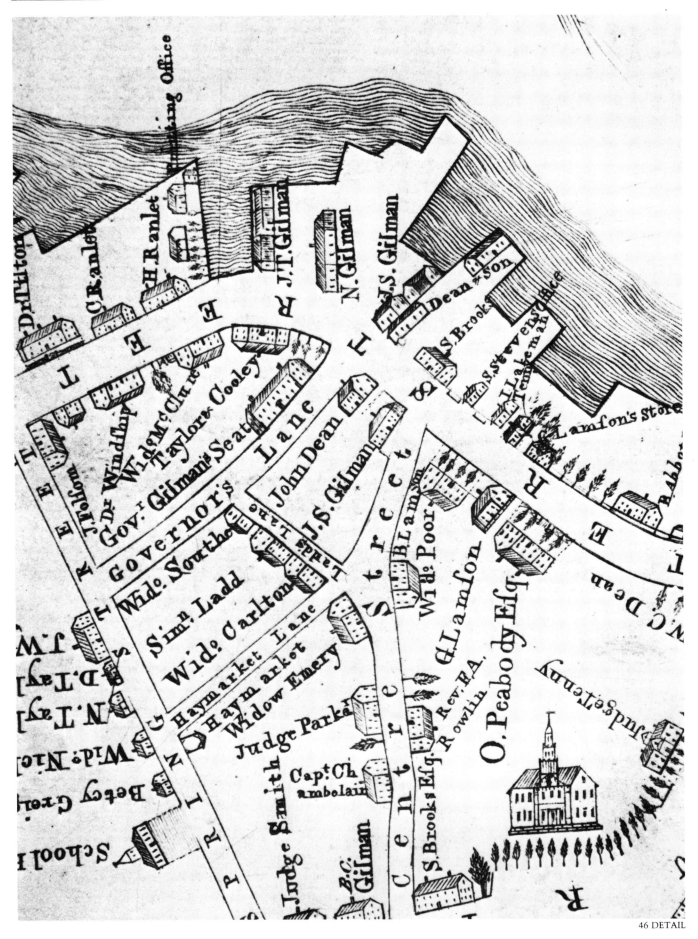

below the two tiers of milldams. Deacon Odiorne's "Duck Manufactory," a Ship Yard, Ship Timber Yard, and associated stores suggest that a significant part of this early industrial activity still involved the building, outfitting, and supplying of ships in the Piscataqua tidal basin.

A Plan of the Town of Portsmouth Including Newcastle (1805) and *Plan of the Town of New-Castle with the adjacent Islands* (1806) illustrate Phinehas Merrill's mature and artistically accomplished cartographic style. Prepared for the 1803 mapping law, they conform to the standard scale of 200 rods to an inch and pay characteristic attention to detail. The Portsmouth map specifies the location of the town pound, the town's ropewalk, two millponds, and "Tucker's barn" (which lay just out of Portsmouth's jurisdiction in the town of Rye). It also cites three "ancient" dwelling houses belonging to the Wentworth and Brewster families and the "ancient Globe tavern," all presumably seventeenth-century structures. The map of New Castle shows the location of Fort Constitution and adjacent to it a side elevation

of the wooden lighthouse built in 1771 under the administration of Governor John Wentworth. An eight-sided structure made of timbers ninety feet high, the lighthouse was lowered to sixty feet in 1854 and torn down in 1879.

The copperplates for *A Plan of the Town of Exeter* and *A Plan of the Compact Part of the Town of Exeter* are part of the collection of the Exeter Public Library. A. M. Peasley, who engraved both plates, is known to have done only three prints in the Exeter-Newburyport (Massachusetts) area from 1802 to 1804. Perhaps he was one of the restless printmakers, like his contemporaries Whittingham and J[ohn] Gilman and James Akin, who left the area after a few years for the more active publishing centers of Boston and Philadelphia.

References: Albee; Adams, Nathaniel; Bell, *Exeter*; Belknap, Jeremy, 3:231; Nelson, 268–73, 300–301; Hurd, 546; Hazlett, 721; Merrill, Phinehas, *Inventory*; Merrill, Samuel, 348–49, 519; N.H., *Laws*, 7:249, 404, 540, 624–625, 843, 907; 8:60, 589, 919; Carrigain; Merrill, Phinehas, *Scholar's Guide*; Bailey, 87; Currier, *Newburyport*, 288; Belknap, Henry W., 4.

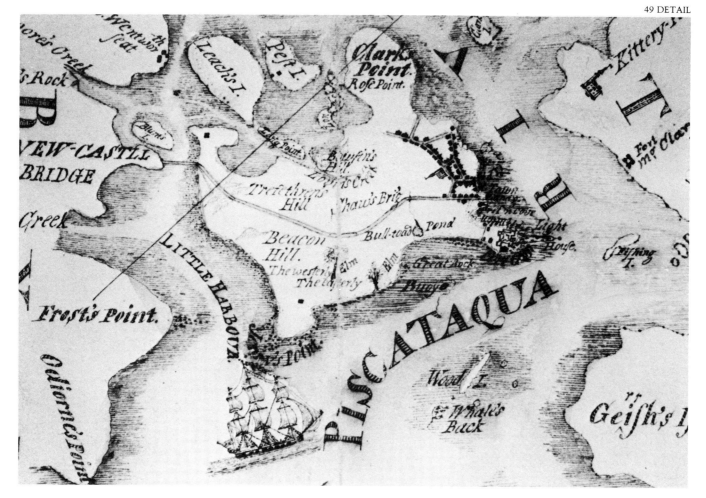

50

**This Harbour of Boston with soundings
without & comings in . . .**

Phillip Wells, cartographer
M. Carroll, draftsman (?)

Boston, circa 1688
Manuscript, ink and watercolor; 22½ ×
17¼ in.
Scale 1:60,000

Boston Public Library

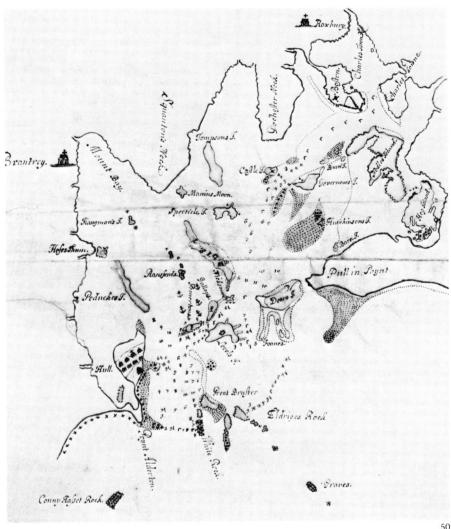

50

The "capitol of New England" (as
Boston was called in the seventeenth
and eighteenth centuries) was the
subject of numerous charts, maps,
and views both in manuscript and
printed form. The earliest focus of
these was Boston Harbor whose islands, peninsulas, ledges, and channels acquired soon after the founding
of Charlestown and Boston a folklore
and toponymy that survive to this
day. The Graves, Hangman's Island,
Spectacles Island, and Halfmoon Island, as well as Bird, Deer, Snake, and
Hog islands reflect the fate of ships
and men, the shape of the land, or the
presumed or actual fauna of individual islands. While the production of
Boston maps and views remained
fairly constant, major changes in administration, colonial wars, revolution, and the promise of profit spurred
new efforts. Like outbreaks of smallpox in Boston, maps and views of the
town came in phases.

The earliest surviving chart of Boston Harbor is a manuscript plan
drawn by Phillip Wells, a land surveyor closely associated with the career of Governor Edmund Andros of
New England, who served under
James II from 1685 to 1689. Purchased
privately at an English auction in
1871, *This Harbour of Boston with
soundings without & comings in* is
probably one of several "Drafts and
Mapps of Boston, Castle Island, the
Harbour & Fortifications" transmit-
ted by Edmund Andros to the Board
of Trade in London sometime after he
received instructions to secure a map
of the area on 7 April 1688 but before
his arrest in Boston on 18 April 1689.
As stated in the legend, the chart was
prepared by Wells under orders from
Andros with the help of four shipmasters, including Captain John Fay-
erweather, who later took command
of the Castle at the time of Andros's
arrest. It was drawn by "M. Carroll"
who has not been identified but who
presumably worked under Wells's su-
pervision.

Little is known of Phillip Wells beyond what can be learned from his
surveys and maps. A 1686 manuscript
by Wells of the American coastline
from the Bay of Honduras to Newfoundland suggests he had cartographic training. His other surviving
productions coincide with the ten-
ures of New York Governor Thomas
Dongan (1682–1688) and New England Governor Edmund Andros
(1685–1689), both of whom he served
as Surveyor General. Wells made a
"sand draught" (coastal chart) of New
York Harbor and a survey of Staten
Island for Dongan in 1684. In the
same year he was appointed one of
the commissioners designated to run
the boundary line between New York
and Connecticut. In New England he
was frequently employed by land
claimants who enjoyed the favor of
the Andros regime (79, 80). His absence from the New England records
after 1688 implies that he returned to
England with Andros or took up another, less controversial occupation.

References: Goodell; Failey, 13, 54; Brad-
ford, 1:174–75; Mass. Archives, Wells;
Trumbull, J. Hammond, "description";
Stokes, 1:232; Tooley, 659.

51

. . . a Sand Draft of the Mattathussetts Bay . . .

Thomas Pound (d. 1703), cartographer
John Harris (fl. 1686–1740), engraver
Phillip Lea, publisher

London, 1691

Engraving with watercolor; partially inset map in Pound's *A New Mapp of New England from Cape Codd to Cape Sable*; 28⅛ × 36⅛ in.

Scale 1:3,000,000 (inset 1:40,000)

Library of Congress

Not long after Phillip Wells completed his composite chart of Boston Harbor, a number of printed plans of the harbor appeared in English and French maritime atlases and pilot books and as individual prints. Among the earliest of these was John Thornton's *Boston harbor in New England*, prepared for his 1689 *English Pilot, The Fourth Book*. Thornton's chart was closely copied by Cyprian Southack whose *A draught of Boston harbor*, engraved by Augus-

tine Fitzhugh, was published in 1694. The English mapmaker Robert Morden offered a small inset of the harbor in his 1695 *A new map of the English empire in America*. The French cartographer Jean Baptiste Franquelin in the meantime had published in 1693 a detailed *Carte de la ville, baye, et environs de Baston*. These examples provide clear evidence of the growing importance of Boston to the larger Atlantic trading system of the seventeenth century; and all were intended to serve, like the Wells map, as navigational charts.

While simulating the appearance of a navigational chart, Captain Thomas Pound's *A New Mapp of New England . . . together with a Sand Draft of the Mattathussetts Bay*, published by Phillip Lea in London about 1690 to 1694, was designed principally as a decorative wall map. Set off with three elaborate dedicatory and explanatory cartouches, Pound's *New Mapp* combines a small-scale "Coast Draft" of northern New England with a larger-scale "Sand Draft" of Boston

Harbor, the latter cleverly occupying the available expanse of open ocean, though at the cost of distorting and lengthening the harbor. Phillip Lea's engraver, John Harris, may have been responsible for an even more grievous error. This is the incorrect alignment of the compass directional pointer twenty degrees to the west of true north. Captain Edmund Halley is quoted in the 1707 *English Pilot* as observing a ten-degree magnetic variation west in the harbor, but with the northern pointer an additional ten degrees in error, the "chart" would be as much a navigational hindrance as an aid.

The configuration of Pound's coastline is scarcely an improvement over that of John Smith's map (3), but his handling of Boston Harbor is clearly based on firsthand experience. In 1687 Thomas Pound was commissioned by Edmund Andros as the pilot of a coastal frigate operating between Cape Sable and Boston. After Andros's fall from power, Thomas Pound joined eleven other Boston shipmas-

51

ters and seamen who pooled their knowledge of the area to engage in a brief career as pirates, successfully preying on small ships off the coasts of New England and Virginia from August through September 1689. After a skirmish with a government sloop, *Mary* (the latter was manned by "brisk *Bostoneers*"), Pound was confined with fourteen other pirates in Boston's jail, together with Mary Glover, the Irish Catholic witch. Condemned to be hanged on 27 January 1690, Pound was reprieved, and he returned to England. Pound's map was dedicated to Charles Gerard, first Earl of Macclesfield, who helped secure Pound's appointment as commander of a channel frigate in August 1690.

References: Walker; Pound; Boston, 25; Charnock, 2:401; Tooley, 516; BL, *Printed*, 10:474; Edmonds; Hitchings, 51, Figure 33.

52 DETAIL

52

A New Plan of yᵉ Great Town of Boston in New England in America . . .

John Bonner (fl. 1719–1726), artist
Francis Dewing, engraver
William Price (1684–1771), publisher

Boston, 1743
Engraving; altered state of a 1722 plate by Dewing; 16⅞ × 23¼ in.
Scale 1:12,000

Boston Public Library

At about the time that printed charts of Boston Harbor became standardized in the *English Pilot* in the early eighteenth century, the increasing sophistication and urbanism of Boston led engravers and publishers to produce maps of the town designed purely for decorative and historical purposes. The first such map was drawn in 1722 by Captain John Bonner, a seventy-seven-year-old shipmaster whose cartographic ability and lifelong interest in maps and charts produced one of the finest large-scale town maps published in colonial America. The original plate of Bonner's *Town of Boston in New England* was engraved by Francis Dewing, a newcomer to the colonies from London (1716), and sold by John Bonner and three other Boston print sellers who were probably co-investors. The Bonner imprint was republished in at least eight later states from 1725 to 1769 by William Price, who acquired ownership of the plate. Each time it was reprinted Price made major revisions and alterations.

A large, detailed map that depicts every street, building, bridge, and windmill in the town, Bonner's *Boston* has a noticeable maritime focus: wharves, shipyards, docks, and warehouses are individually named and furnished with flotillas at dockside and in the harbor. In style, however, the map conforms to vernacular land maps or working surveys being produced in Europe and lacks the sophistication of English or European decorative town maps. Buildings are shown in elevation as viewed from the street; wharves, with ships alongside, as seen from water level. A capsule history of Boston is offered through a listing of "Great Fires," outbreaks of "Gener.[11] Small Pox" and a notation that the town contained "Streets 42 Lanes 36 and Alleys 22."

The 1743 issue of the Bonner map, titled *A New Plan of ye Great Town of Boston in New England in America,* represents a late stage in the evolution of Dewing's plate. The eleven meetinghouses shown in 1722 (A through L) have been supplemented by eight more (M through T); one additional outbreak of smallpox has been recorded; most of the harbor has been taken up by Price's dedication,

by his advertisements, and by a short history of the town. Two more fires and the building of Thomas Hancock's stone mansion overlooking Boston Common were still to be added to the 1760 and 1769 issues of the plate, but virtually all other available space had been filled up. Despite naive elements, John Bonner's map and William Price's subsequent issues of it constitute an important chapter in early American decorative mapping. No other New England town inspired a comparable series until the publication of Phinehas Merrill's maps of Stratham and Exeter (44–47) and James Wadsworth's map of New Haven (65) in the late eighteenth and early nineteenth centuries.

References: Reps; Boston, 33–47; Waite.

52 DETAIL

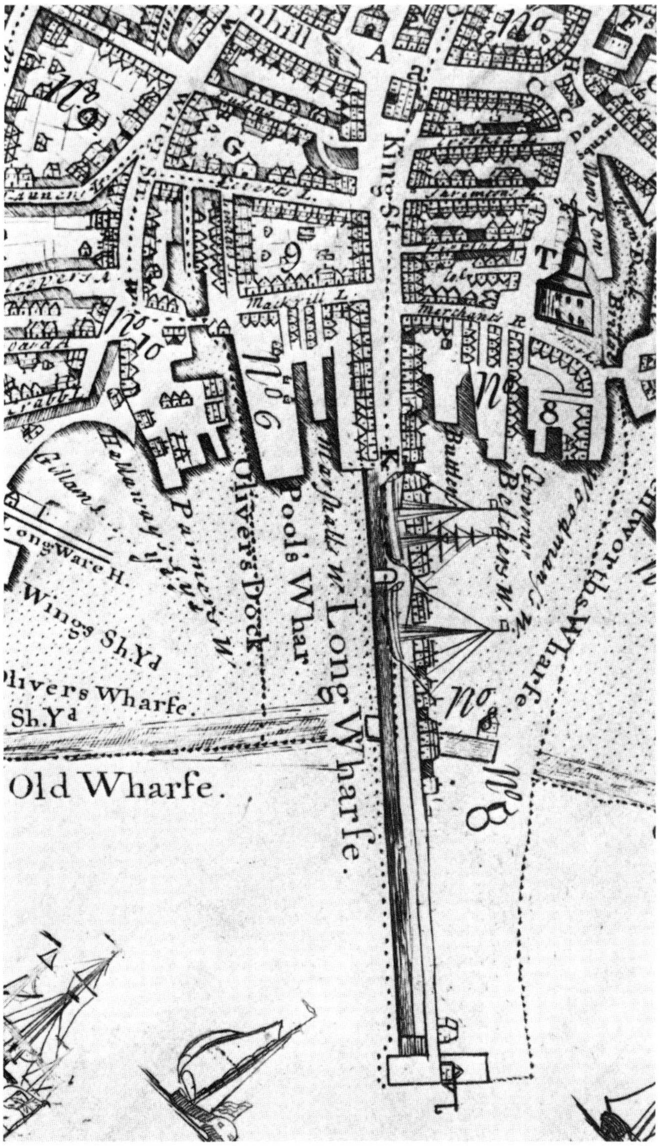

53 DETAIL

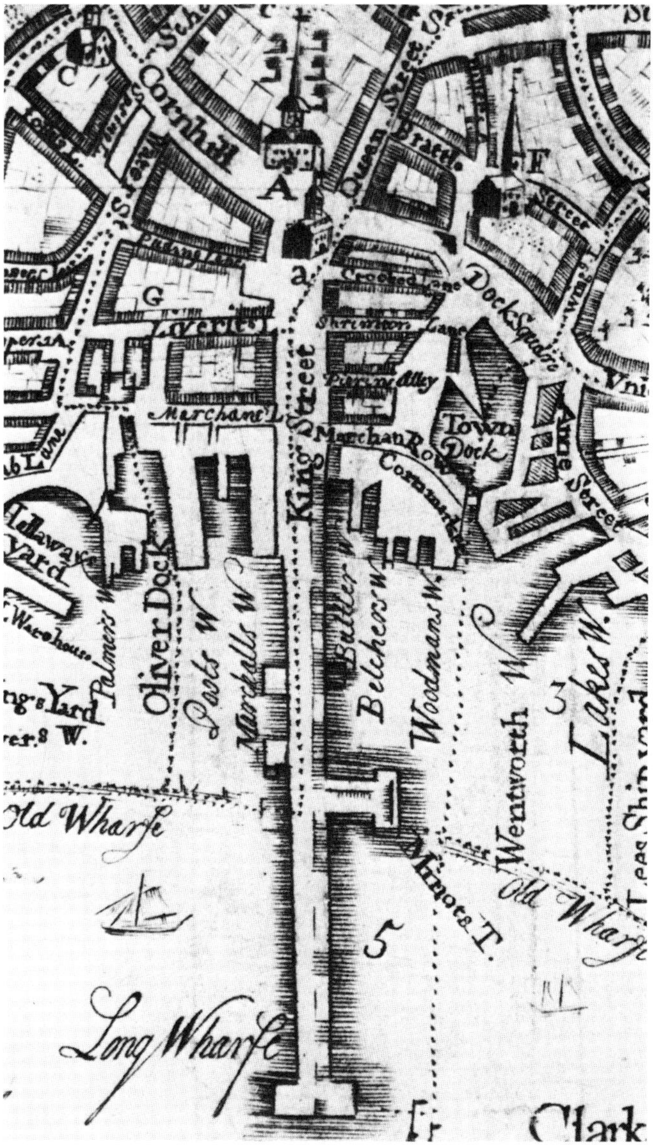

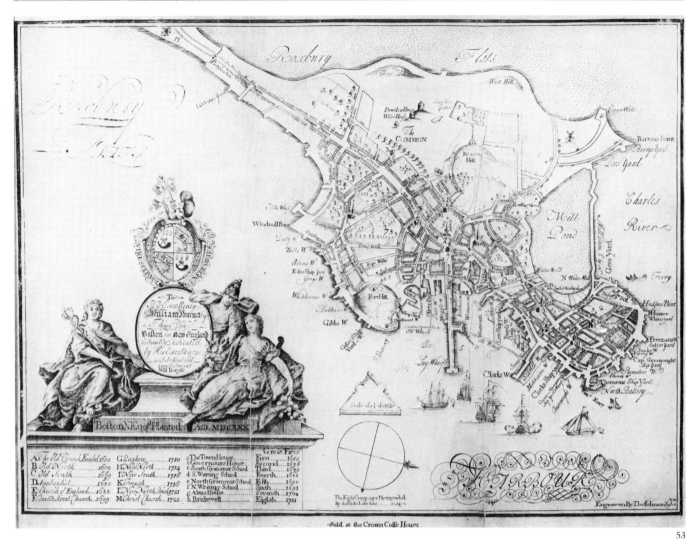

53

Boston N Eng.d Planted A.D. MDCXXX

William Burgis (fl. 1716–1731), artist
Thomas Johnston (circa 1708–1767), engraver

Boston, 1728
Engraving; 12 × 15¼ in.
Scale 1:10,000
Library of the Boston Athenaeum

Six years after Captain John Bonner issued *The Town of Boston*, William Burgis published his 1728 *Boston NEng.d Planted A.D. MDCXXX*, which imitated Bonner's plan in a smaller format but which was more professionally executed. An English designer and publisher recently active in New York, William Burgis, like William Price, was a member of Boston's Anglican community. He had previously issued a northeast view of the town (121). His new plate was engraved by Thomas Johnston of Boston, who was trained in Europe and who is believed to have made the later alterations to Dewing's plate of the Bonner map (52).

William Burgis's map shows most buildings as shaded blocks lining the streets. His imitation of Bonner included his using the same letter symbols for identifying the meetinghouses and churches. He did, however, offer perspective views of individual meetinghouses, churches, windmills, powder houses, and shipyards the detail of which adds to the understanding of eighteenth-century ecclesiastic, commercial, and municipal architecture. He also added to Bonner's design the eight "Companys" or wards into which the town had been divided. Burgis's map is known in one state; only two prints have survived. Following the European style, the map component of the print is almost an afterthought to a composition dominated by the dedicatory cartouche addressed to Massachusetts Governor William Burnet.

References: Holman, "Burgis"; Reps; Boston, 38–39; Wheat and Brun, 50–53.

54

Boston its Environs and Harbour, with the Rebels Works Raised Against That Town in 1775

Thomas Hyde Page (1746–1821) and John Montresor (1736–1799), cartographers

William Faden, engraver

London, 1 October 1778

Engraving with watercolor; altered state of a 1777 plate; 18¼ × 26½ in.

Scale 1:30,000

The Bostonian Society

Responding to popular demand, English publishers issued numerous maps of Boston illustrating the military topography of the town during the months from May 1775 through March 1776 when British forces in Boston were under siege by patriot troops in surrounding Roxbury, Dorchester, Cambridge, and Medford. The most desirable source for such maps was the work of surveyors and military engineers attached to the British forces — in particular, the manuscript maps of a gifted young engineer named John Montresor who later became Chief Engineer for the English forces in America. William Faden's *Boston its Environs and Harbour, with the Rebels Works Raised Against That Town in 1775*, published in 1778, was based on maps and charts supplied to him in 1777 by John Montresor and Thomas Hyde Page, both serving in the Corps of Engineers at the time of the siege. Primarily a chart of Boston Harbor that shows channels, depths, sandbars, and flats, the plan also provides the location and design of the principal siege-works around the town and the English defensive works at Roxbury Neck and at Charlestown. The style and cartographic vocabulary closely resemble John Montresor's known manuscript work. Elevations are shown by stippling and coloration.

Cultivated fields are shown by dotted lines. Maps of revolutionary Boston continued to be popular in England even after the English evacuation of the town and the subsequent shift in the war's focus to the middle and southern colonies.

The third-generation member of a line of English military engineers, John Montresor was the son of James Montresor and the subject of a 1790 novel by Susanna Rowson of Boston titled *Charlotte Temple*. William Faden, formerly in partnership with Thomas Jefferys, was geographer to George III; it was this latter connection that probably gave him access to military maps and charts.

References: Tooley, 201, 485, 446; Marshall; Stevens and Tree; Boston, 58–59; Klemp, Map 40; PRO, 2:2512.

54 DETAIL

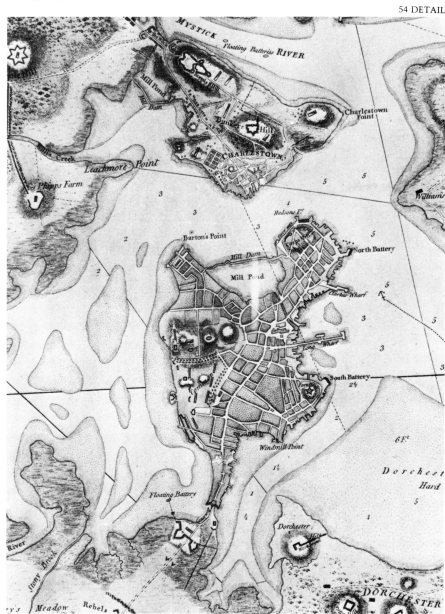

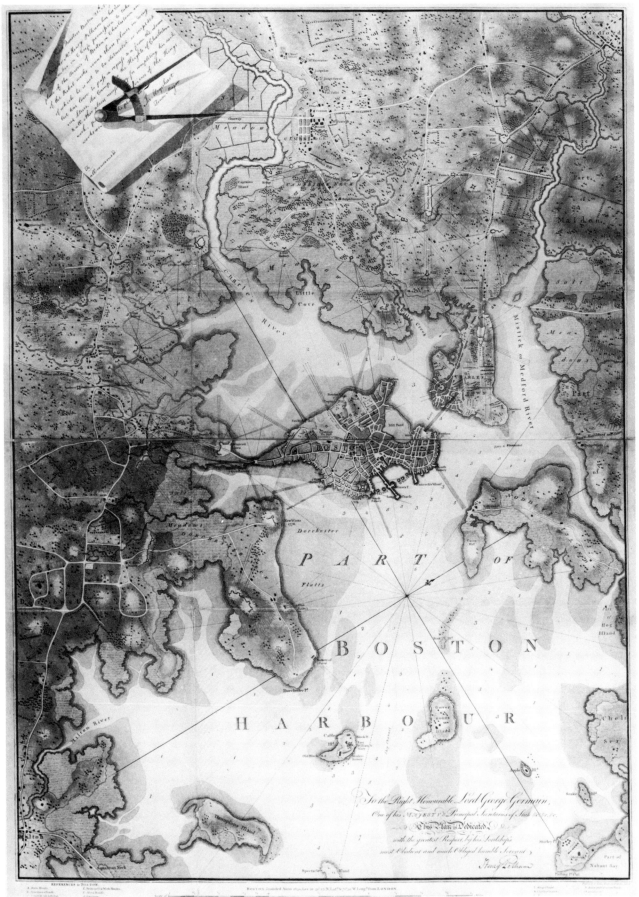

55

A Plan of Boston in New England with its Environs

Henry Pelham (1748–1806), artist
Francis Jukes (1745–1812), engraver
London, 1777
Aquatint; 27 ⅜ × 38¾ in. (sight)
Scale 1:14,000
Boston Public Library

Besides military maps and charts, resourceful English map publishers also drew on the talents of disenchanted or exiled American loyalists who left Boston at the time of its evacuation in March 1776. One such loyalist was Henry Pelham, son of the portraitist Peter Pelham of Boston and half brother of the painter John Singleton Copley. Pelham, who had learned to draw from Copley, had been instructed by the English commanders in Boston to "take a plan" of Boston and Charlestown and the "Rebel works" surrounding them. When he arrived in London the following year, Pelham took his notes and drawings to the engraver Francis Jukes and published *A Plan of Boston in New England with its Environs,* as it was seen during 1775 and 1776, with a dedication to Lord George Germain, one of the King's secretaries of state. A native of the Boston area, Pelham was intimately familiar with its topography, particularly of towns such as Cambridge, where he plotted individual Tory estates along Brattle Street. He employed advanced cartographic techniques to show land relief and hydrography and added a touch of realism with the pass note and compass artfully laid in the upper left-hand corner. Pelham noted military details with equal accuracy: the "New Works 1776," whose installation forced the English to evacuate Boston, is correctly located on Puller's Hill in Dorchester Heights.

Like most Boston artists and printmakers, Henry Pelham was a member of the town's Anglican community. His religious bias is revealed, perhaps, in his individually naming the Anglican churches of the town (I, K, and L) but collectively labeling the ten Congregational meetinghouses M. Despite his Tory sympathies, Henry Pelham's views about the war were mixed. It was Pelham's *Fruits of Arbitrary Power,* illustrating the 1770 Boston Massacre, that Paul Revere plagiarized for *The Bloody Massacre.* Pelham's wartime letters to his half brother in London regretfully noted the "terrible changes in the landscape" and the destruction of Charlestown and the loss of a "Great Number of Wooden Houses" in Boston to provide "fewel" for the occupying army.

References: Boston, 53; *American Printmaking,* 27; *Revere's Boston,* 113, 137; Reps; PRO, 2:2515.

56

Plan of Boston

Benjamin West (1730–1812), publisher
Connecticut, 1776 (Norwich)
Woodcut; 6⅜ × 4¼ in.
Published in West's *Bickerstaff's New England Almanack*
Scale 1:30,000
Boston Public Library

Like their English counterparts, American publishers responded to popular interest in the patriot siege of Boston by producing maps identifying the topography of the region and the location of the opposing forces. The *Plan of Boston,* a small woodcut included in a New England almanac published by Benjamin West for the year 1776, consists of a detailed map of Boston peninsula and an inset of the harbor. The American positions in Roxbury and in Charlestown are located by zigzag lines and pictographic forts. Principal features are coded by letters and explained in detail on the opposite page. A self-taught astronomer and mathematics

56

teacher at Rhode Island College, Benjamin West began publishing almanacs in 1763. Within four years his success was so great that editions were issued simultaneously in Boston, Salem, Norwich, and Providence. The pseudonym "Isaac Bickerstaff" had been used in English literature for over sixty years when he selected it for the name of his Boston edition, and many later "Bickerstaff" almanacs published in America had no connection with West.

References: DAB, 20:5; Reps.

57

Boston Harbour

Lydia Withington (1784–1869)

Boston, 30 June 1799

Satin, embroidered in silk; 24 × 19 in.
Scale 1:40,000

The Bostonian Society

The publication of maps of Boston and Boston Harbor in popular magazines in the late eighteenth century eventually led to their use as subjects for needlework compositions. *Boston Harbour*, a map sampler worked by Lydia Withington while at Mrs. Susanna Rowson's School in Boston in 1799, is copied from a print in the *Pennsylvania Magazine* of June 1775. The print is itself derived closely from the inset map "A Plan of Boston Harbor from an Accurate Survey" in the lower right-hand section of Braddock Mead's 1755 *Map of the most Inhabited part of New England* (12, 13) and consequently shows little evidence of the military events that prompted its appearance in the magazine. Lydia Withington's choice of subject may not have been accidental. A cousin of the Dorchester surveyor and mapmaker Mather Withington, who prepared surveys of Mattapan, Quincy, and Roxbury, she probably executed the work as a gift for a member of her family.

Surviving needlework maps are rare. Lydia Withington's *Boston Harbour* is the only known example of a New England subject. More common are English needlework maps of England, English counties, or continental subjects, brought to New England as gifts by American shipmasters.

References: Huish, 92–95; Cabot, 46–47; Dorchester, 671.

58

This is a spot of land which Chebaco men propounded for to the towne of Ipswich to sit a meeting house on . . .

Unknown draftsman

Massachusetts, 1667
Manuscript, ink; 14¾ × 11¼ in.
Scale 1:40,000

Massachusetts Archives

One of the most common forms of public mapping undertaken in early New England was the demographic survey prepared to accompany a petition for parish or town status or the location or relocation of a meetinghouse. These surveys were sometimes the focus of intense controversy for two reasons: first, because parish separations reduced the tax base of the parent town; and second, because a meetinghouse location that was convenient for one group of families was often inconvenient for another. When the residents of the south or Chebacco district of Ipswich applied to the General Court of the Massachusetts Bay Colony for parish status in 1667, they prepared a sketch map (58) to accompany their written petition showing the locations of the dwelling houses around the Chebacco River in relation to a "spot of land" that they had selected as the site of the proposed meetinghouse. The purpose of the sketch was to persuade the court that enough families were now living in Chebacco to justify the formation of a separate parish. Forty-two dwelling houses are shown, and presumably more were located within the compass star. The petition noted that none of these lay more than two and a half miles from the proposed center. By way of contrast, some of these same houses were seven and a half miles distant from the existing Ipswich meetinghouse. The petition pointed out that a new parish would allow the Chebacco residents to "go home comfortably to theyir own houses and refresh themselves the midst of the day." It also pointed out that these same residents presently lived "under the sin of the breach of the sabbath." "We ask," the petition concluded, "and humbly request the honored general court to prevent so much traveling on the sabath day if it may be." When the second or Chebacco parish in Ipswich was recognized in 1679, the actual site selected for the meetinghouse was approximately one mile southwest of the center of the compass star in the 1667 sketch. Chebacco remained a parish of the town of Ipswich until it was incorporated as the present town of Essex.

The distances cited in the Chebacco petition offer an insight into the origin of the six-mile-square township. Residents living within a mile or two miles of the meetinghouse could conveniently return home on foot between the morning and afternoon Sabbath service. Those living up to three miles distant might not return home for refreshment but could petition for permission to build Sabbath-day houses as a substitute. Those living more than three miles distant probably missed either the morning or afternoon service and at best attended on a seasonal basis only.

References: "Essay"; Choate, 84; Felt, 257.

58 DETAIL

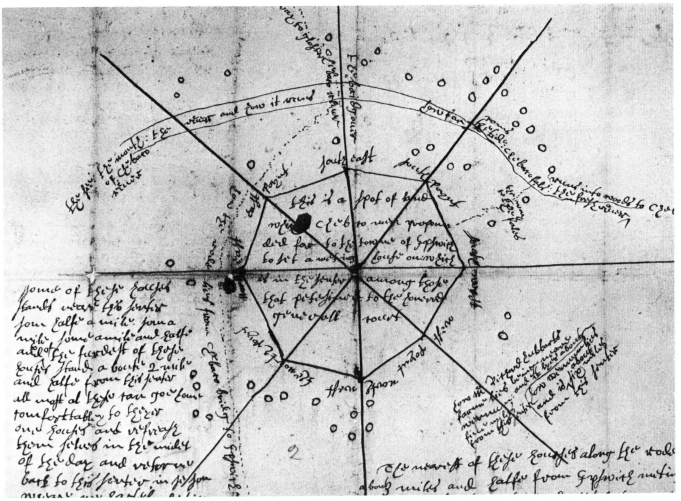

59

. . . the several devisions of marthas vineyard . . .

Simon Athearn

Massachusetts, circa 1692
Manuscript, ink; 10¾ × 14 in.
Scale 1:120,000

Massachusetts Archives

In 1692 a warrant from Governor William Phips requesting representatives to the next session of the "great and General Court" in Boston informed the residents of Martha's Vineyard that their island had been transferred from New York to Massachusetts jurisdiction. The news upset the island's traditional power structure; and the Mayhew family, which stood to lose most from this change, immediately sent word to New York for confirmation and advice. Other islanders, such as Simon Athearn, tried to make the best of a confused situation by contacting the new Boston authorities in a series of communications that is now preserved in the Massachusetts Archives. Athearn wished to accomplish three things: to identify and confirm the traditional territorial and municipal jurisdictions of the island; to consolidate Chilmark, Tisbury, and other western areas into one single ecclesiastical parish; and to make a formal request to the court to allow that one individual (rather than two or more) represent the fifty-eight families on the island as well as those on the neighboring Elizabeth Islands.

Athearn's *several devisions of marthas vineyard,* which accompanied his communications, is the earliest known detailed map of the island. A schematic map, it identifies the principal boundary points and bodies of water but does not show their true configurations or size relationships. One tract of land that was still in dispute is identified by the phrase "John Mayhews children who hath the most rights to it." "Holms his hole," an inlet on the northern side of the island, occurs several times in Athearn's description. Like "Wood's Hole" and "Robinson's Hole" on the southern end of Cape Cod, this naming pattern may have been local in origin since it is found with some frequency in Cape Cod and the Islands.

References: Banks, 1:182–85.

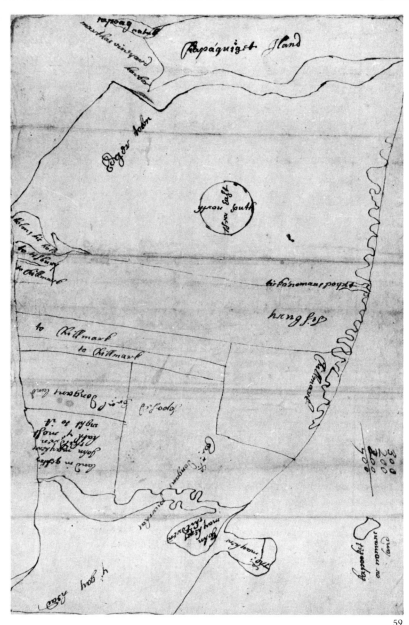

59

60

a platt of the township of Sudbury . . .

John Brigham (1645–1728)

Massachusetts, 1708
Manuscript, ink; 20¾ × 13¾ in.
Scale 1:36,000

Massachusetts Archives

The division of Sudbury into eastern and western precincts, and the subdivision of the two precincts into the constituent towns of Wayland, Sudbury, Stow, and Maynard, followed an evolutionary pattern common to many early New England towns, particularly those whose boundaries in any way exceeded the traditional six-mile-square layout. In this pattern the initial proprietors and settlers built their meetinghouse at an easterly location convenient to them but some distance from the geographical center of the township. As the town gradually filled up, the original meetinghouse site became increasingly burdensome to the town's newer, western residents who would petition to move the site to the center of the town or to form a second precinct.

In Sudbury, a five-mile-square town chartered in 1639, the usual pattern was reinforced by the existence of the Sudbury River, which divided the town into east bank and west bank residents, and by the so-called Two-mile Grant distributed in 1658, which extended the town's limits an additional two miles westward. The first petition by the west-siders was submitted to the General Court of Massachusetts in 1707. Claiming they were "forced for to seek our spiritual good with the peril of our Lives" (that is, fording the icy river), the petitioners noted that some west-side residents were required to travel as much as three to six miles. "Many of our children and little ones," the document added, "[and] ancient and weak persons, can very Rarly attend the public worship." The petition was opposed by a majority of the town, including a number of west-side residents who preferred to put up with the inconvenience of travel rather than bear the expense of a separate minister and meetinghouse. The court turned down the petition. Undaunted, the west-side group petitioned again the following year, and this time they succeeded and won recognition as the second parish in Sudbury. But they did not take advantage of their option until thirteen years later, in 1721.

John Brigham, a doctor, surveyor, and aggressive land speculator, was a proprietor of Sudbury. A resident of the west side of the Sudbury River, he was among those who petitioned for separation in 1707. In 1708 he prepared *a platt of the township of Sudbury* on which "the several houses on each side of the great River with the farmers adjacent" were indicated with the letter *h*. The map locates 120 dwelling houses, 49 on the east side of the Sudbury River (where the original meetinghouse was situated) and 59 on the west side and in the two-mile grant. In the schematic location of the dwelling houses on the east side can still be seen the contours of the "Puritan Village" of Sudbury as it was laid out in 1639–1649 with two common fields and a cow common. When the younger or second parish of Sudbury became incorporated as a town, it retained the name of Sudbury. The first parish, or original village, became the town of Wayland.

References: Hudson, 124–25, 285–89; Brigham, 70–71; Powell, 126–27.

60

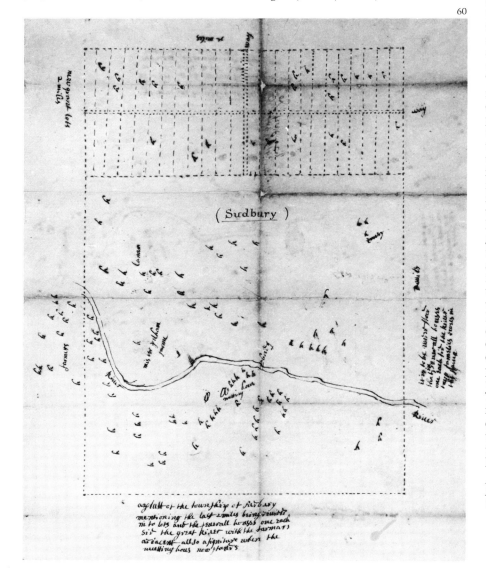

61

[Parish Division, Watertown]

Samuel Thaxter

Massachusetts, 1720
Manuscript, ink; 17 × 13½ in.
Scale 1:40,000

Massachusetts Archives

The original boundaries of Watertown, Massachusetts, were much larger than could reasonably accommodate the spatial ideal of a meetinghouse located centrally within a six-mile-square area. As in nearby Sudbury (60), the town's initial settlers erected a meetinghouse in the eastern corner of the town; the site was convenient to a majority of the town in 1633 but was inaccessible to families holding lots in the central and western portions of Watertown during the last quarter of the seventeenth century. When a sufficient number of dwelling houses had been built and occupied by the western farmers, the town agreed to maintain two ministers and two meetinghouses, in effect sidestepping the usual legal procedures that would have divided the town into two ecclesiastic districts. The 1720 plan outlining the boundaries, principal roads, and locations of dwelling houses in Watertown was prepared by Samuel Thaxter after the town realized that joint support of two meetinghouses and two ministers was too unwieldy and that a parish division would be beneficial. (The issue was further complicated by the fact that neither meetinghouse site was convenient.) Thaxter's initial line left 82 houses in the east congregation and 104 in the west congregation. However, when Thaxter moved a southerly section of the line approximately three-quarters of a mile westward, 12 homes in the western sector were transferred to the eastern sector, leaving 94 dwelling houses in the eastern district and 92 in the western one. The names of the twelve heads of household affected by this proposed shift, together with a thirteenth, are listed numerically on Thaxter's document and are identified by number at their respective locations. The present division between the towns of Watertown and Waltham generally follows Thaxter's line.

References: Sanderson, 34–35; Convers, 70–71; Watertown, 316–19.

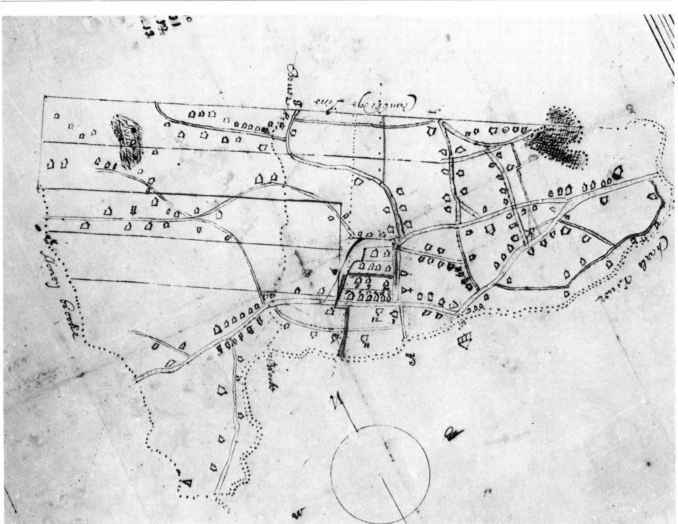

61

62*

A Plan of the West Parish or Newbury new Town

John Brown (b. 1683)

Massachusetts, 1729

Lithograph by Tappan & Bradford, Boston, circa 1850; 26⅛ × 22 in.

Based on a manuscript by Brown

Scale 1:18,000

Historical Society of Old Newbury

Newbury, Massachusetts, a farming, fishing, and maritime community located at the mouth of the Merrimack River, grew so rapidly in the seventeenth and eighteenth centuries that at one time it encompassed seven legally recognized ecclesiastical parishes, three Anglican churches, and one Quaker meeting. The fourth ecclesiastic division in the town was initiated in 1729 by a petition drawn by the upper or western residents of the second parish who noted they had "near eight score dwelling houses, besides churchmen and quakers." In a document dated 28 August 1729, they

requested the Massachusetts General Court to divide the second parish along Whit Street and Balley's Lane. The upper residents were so confident of success they had already erected a substantial (fifty by thirty-eight feet) two-story meetinghouse even before submitting their appeal. (It is shown as number 120 near the junction of Hobmans and Moses lanes.) Two years later they were recognized as the fourth parish of Newbury.

Dated 15 September 1729, John Brown's *Plan of the West Parish or Newbury new Town* was probably commissioned by the Massachusetts General Court in its review of the August 28 separation petition. It indicates the location and ownership of 183 dwelling houses and shows with a dotted line the proposed division between the "Standing part" and the "New Parrish." Brown's map is more carefully and professionally prepared than most known examples of its type. It reveals that the second parish had grown to the point of requiring an extensive road network. It also reveals that a plurality of dwelling

houses (75 out of 183) lay on a single principal east-west road that ran roughly parallel with the Merrimack River.

A *Plan of the West Parish* is known only as a lithographic copy made in the nineteenth century. "John Brown, Surv.," who drew the original in 1729, was probably the John Brown who lived on the southwesterly side of Turkey hills in the "Standing Part" of the parish and who as a twelve-year-old boy was kidnapped by a party of Indians. (His house is shown as number 185 on the map.) The area occupied by dwelling houses 4 through 7 (owned by John, Thomas, Seth, and Samuel Bartlett) is shown on a contemporary watercolor sketch map of the Merrimack River (68) as Bartlett's Point and Bartlett's Cove.

References: Coffin, 200; Currier, *History of Newbury,* 229–36; Currier, *Ould Newbury,* 288.

. . . plan of the Roads and the Scituation of the Houses in the parish of Natick

Samuel Livermore (circa 1705–1773)

Massachusetts, 1 August 1749
Manuscript, ink; 10½ × 13¼ in.
Scale 1:46,000

Massachusetts Archives

A meetinghouse-site controversy that involved a more complex issue than the convenience of travel took place in Natick, a seventeenth-century praying Indian village that in the eighteenth century reverted to English ownership as the native Algonquian population dwindled and died out. The original meetinghouse in Natick, built by the Indian missionary John Eliot in 1651 to serve approximately thirty Algonquian families, was located in the southern sector of the parish. When this structure was replaced by a second, larger structure in 1721, no English families had yet settled in the parish. (Some English had settled in so-called Needham Leg, an area of land that jutted into the parish but that remained under Dedham jurisdiction.) When a third meetinghouse was proposed for this site in 1747, however, the English population in the parish proper probably outnumbered that of the Indians; additionally, Needham Leg was placed within its jurisdiction. So many of the new English families were now located in the northern and western sectors of the parish that they, and the Needham Leg residents, requested the provincial General Court to approve a site in the center of town located on Peagun Plain. But this site was inconvenient to a majority of the Indians. The issue was complicated by the fact that the minister of the Natick church, Oliver Peabody (served 1721–1752), like his successor Stephen Badger (served 1753–1774), was supported by the Commissioners for Propagating the Gospel in New England rather than by parish or provincial taxes. Before settling the matter, the General Court took under advisement a report from the English guardians of the Indian interests in Natick, as well as petitions from a number of English inhabitants of Needham Leg who asked to be excused from taxes so that they might again attend meeting in the adjoining west precinct of Dedham. At the same time the court also commissioned Samuel Livermore of Watertown to make a survey of the parish. Three manuscript copies of Livermore's *plan of the Roads and the Scituation of the Houses in the parish of Natick,* dated 1 August 1749, are in the Massachusetts Archives. Because the issue involved a conflict between Indian and English rights, Livermore was careful to note which dwelling houses were occupied by English families (red dots) and which were occupied by Indian fam-

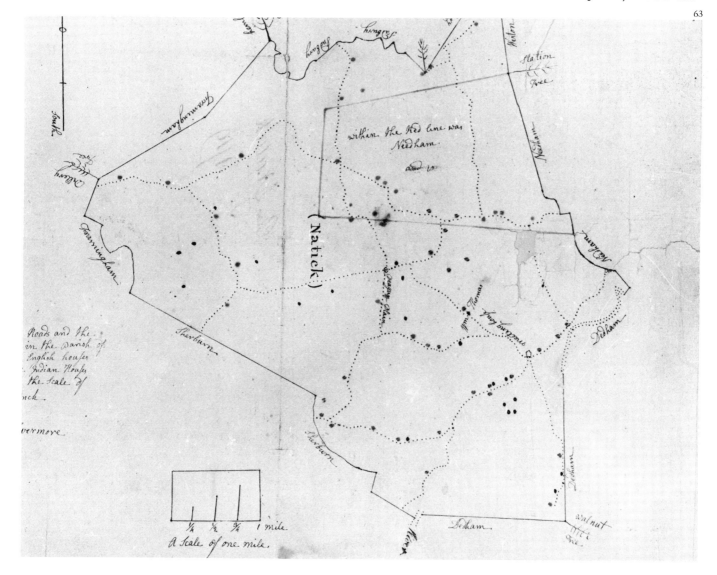

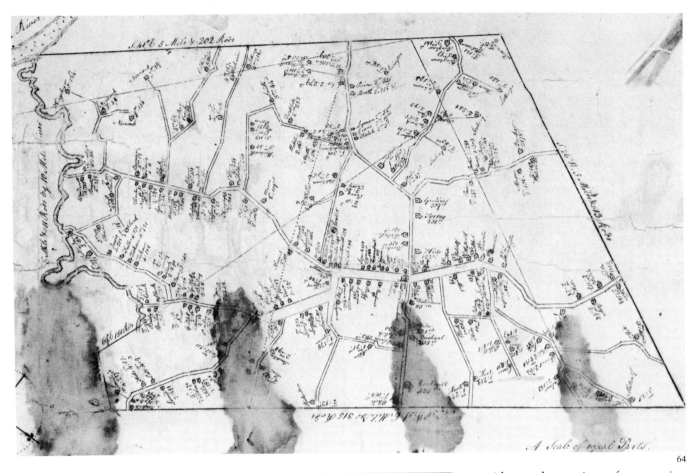

64

ilies (black dots). The forty-five English homes outnumber the Indian homes by approximately two to one, most of them, unlike the Indian homes and wigwams, located on the town's principal roads. The Court turned down the English petition to move the site and denied the English the option of paying taxes in Dedham. In 1761 Natick became a normal, taxed English parish. However, the removal of the meetinghouse to a central site did not occur until 1799 when the English population of the town had grown to about 700 and the Indian population had dwindled to about 150.

A resident of the western precinct in Watertown, Samuel Livermore inherited the "Lyman Farm" from his granduncle Nathaniel Livermore. He was a Justice of the Peace for Middlesex County and served Watertown as a town selectman for twenty-two years and as town clerk, town assessor, and representative to the General Court.

References: Clarke, 140–53; Bacon, 27–28, 41, 108–9; Bond, 1:345; Notes, 15; Mass. Archives, Livermore, Natick.

64

A Plan of the first Society in Lebanon . . .
Nathaniel Webb
Connecticut, 1772
Manuscript, ink; 17½ × 23 in.
Scale 1:28,000
Yale University Library

Perhaps no site controversy in New England stirred more extreme behavior than the 109-year "meetinghouse war" waged in the first society in Lebanon, Connecticut, which pitted the older families in the southeastern district against the newer, increasingly numerous families of the northern and western districts. The controversy originated in 1697 when the proprietors and settlers of Lebanon agreed among themselves that the meetinghouse was to be "forever" fixed on the broad street or highway in the southeast sector of the town. When the town proposed to replace the first meetinghouse with a new one in 1724, residents in the northwestern sector offered so much opposition to the old location that the effort was stalled. A 1731 committee appointed by the Connecticut General Assembly ruled in favor of the old site, while allowing the northwest

residents the option of recovering their share of the cost of the new building if they formed their own society. The northwest residents did not exercise their option, however. When the society proposed to build a new meetinghouse on a more northerly site in 1772, the southeast residents appealed to the General Assembly, which for a second time honored the "ancient agreement." Again the court gave the northwest faction the option of building separately. No action was taken, and here the matter rested until 1802 when the society as a whole once more voted for a new meetinghouse on a compromise site.

This time, however, the northwest faction anticipated the southerners' reaction and persuaded the General Assembly to give the southerners the option of forming a meetinghouse society and to allow the society as a whole to build on a new northern site. This stratagem proved successful until it came time to tear down the old building; on the day appointed, large crowds assembled at the site to prevent (or to ensure) demolition. The resulting acts of violence, arrests, counterarrests, and court writs saw a number of the town's leading citizens confined in jail and caused a general breakdown of legal processes. The affair was finally settled in 1806 with a financial judgment against the southeast faction that allowed them the right to rebuild the recently demolished meetinghouse at their own cost.

Nathaniel Webb's *Plan of the first Society in Lebanon,* surveyed and drafted in October and November 1772, was one of a series of surveys of Lebanon that were ordered by the Connecticut General Assembly between 1767 and 1772 to help settle the controversy. Webb's plan is unusually detailed and informative. The location of each dwelling house is given by a pictograph with the surname of the owner; the distance of each house from the meetinghouse is given in miles and rods as computed by the shortest route on the existing roads.

_____

References: Kelly, 1:263–74; Webb; Hine, 71–84; Thompson, 36, 38; Garvan, 63–65.

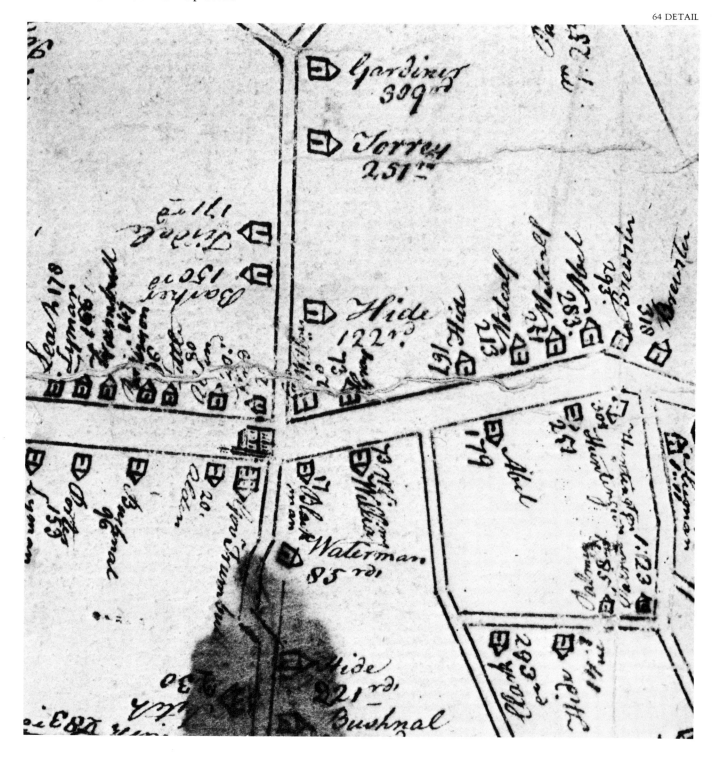

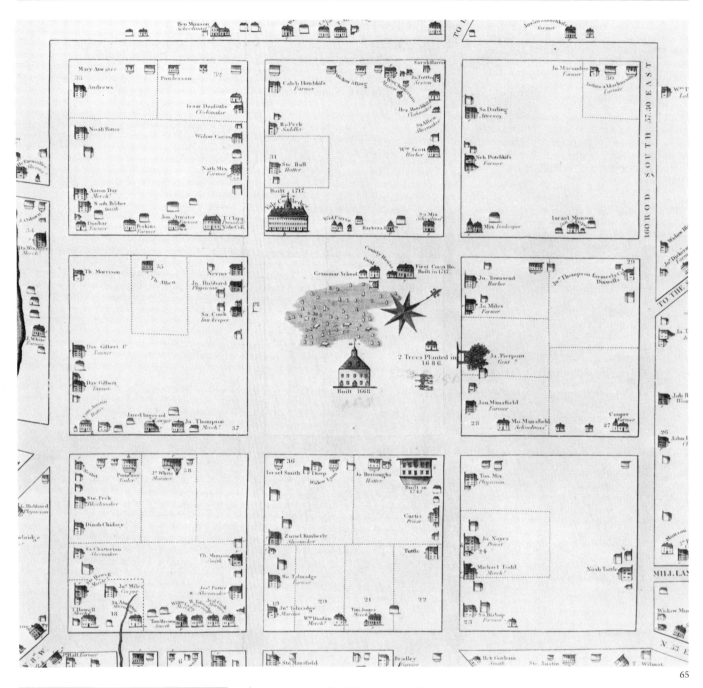

65

A Plan of the Town of New Haven With all the Buildings . . .

James Wadsworth (1730–1817)

Connecticut, 1748

Engraving with watercolor dated 1806 by Thomas Kensett of New Haven (1786–1829) after a manuscript by Wadsworth; 27 × 19½ in.

Scale 1:2,500

New Haven Colony Historical Society

In his senior year at Yale College in 1748, James Wadsworth surveyed and drew a map of New Haven with all of its meetinghouses, dwelling houses,

barns, and outbuildings identified by owner and by owner's occupation. Like most eighteenth-century New England mapmakers, Wadsworth combined technical and naive elements in his plan. He gave the bearings and the lengths of the principal side streets, but table tombs in the center burying ground were shown in three-quarter bird's-eye perspective and all buildings were shown in front elevation as they would be viewed from the nearest street. A number of structures were shown with a framed or hewn overhang. A numbered code identified the original owners of the town lots. Two manuscript copies of the Wadsworth map survive at the

Yale libraries. The unsigned *Plan of the City of New Haven Taken in 1748* may be the original Wadsworth document, though the use of the term *City* suggests it is not. The *Plan of the Town of New Haven with the buildings in 1748, taken by permission from the original of the hon*[ble] *general Wadsworth of Durham . . . 1807* is a copy of the original made, while it was still in Wadsworth's possession, by William Lyon for the Connecticut Academy of Arts and Sciences. Thomas Kensett's *Plan of the Town of New Haven With all the Buildings*, a colored engraving published in New Haven in January 1806, was probably taken from an earlier

William Lyon copy of Wadsworth's map, not the one now in the Yale Library. Kensett coded the buildings *r* and *b* to indicate which should be colored red or blue, and he included Lyon's dedication to the Connecticut Academy of Arts and Sciences. The Kensett engraving is the earliest published map of New Haven. Wadsworth's original is probably the single most important map and architectural inventory produced in New England in the eighteenth century.

Born in Durham, Connecticut, James Wadsworth served as Durham town clerk for thirty years. During the Revolutionary War he held a commission as a colonel and brigadier-general in the Connecticut militia. He represented Connecticut at the Continental Congress from 1783 through 1786.

References: Lyman; Garvan, 44–49.

66

[Map of Newport]

Ezra Stiles (1727–1795)

Rhode Island, 1759
Manuscript, ink; 15 × 12⅜ in. (sight)
Scale 1:5,000

Redwood Library

An architectural inventory of a more technical nature than the James Wadsworth map of New Haven (65) was drawn by Ezra Stiles, who graduated from Yale two years before Wadsworth and who served as pastor of the Second Congregational Church in Newport from 1756 to 1777. Gifted with a prolific, inquiring mind, Stiles conceptualized historic events in cartographic terms — much as the historians Justin Winsor, I. N. Phelps Stokes, John Warner Barber, Howard M. Chapin, and John G. Kohl were to do in the nineteenth and twentieth centuries. Scores of sketch maps are found among Stiles's papers and correspondence, some of them now in

published form. In June, July, and August of 1758 — the second year of his ministry in Newport — Stiles paced off the lengths of the major roads in Newport and recorded the number of dwelling houses, outbuildings, churches, wharves, and landmarks, locating them on a map by a code. The numeral 2 indicated "Houses two Stories"; numeral 1, houses with one story; the letter *S* "Stores, Stillhouses, Shops, Stables, indifferently"; a slashed numeral 2 for "Houses 2 Story wth. 2 Chimneys." By his calculation, the town in 1758 consisted of 140 dwellings with two floors; 48 single-floor dwellings; and 110 stores, shops, stables, and stillhouses.

When the English occupation of Newport dispersed his congregation, Stiles removed to Portsmouth, New Hampshire, to become pastor of the North Church. A year later he accepted the presidency of Yale College.

References: Appleton's, 5:687–88; Stiles, Ezra; Downing.

66 DETAIL

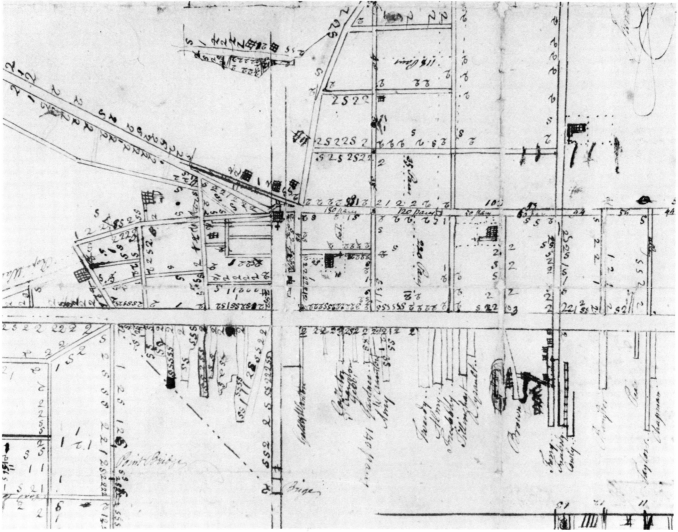

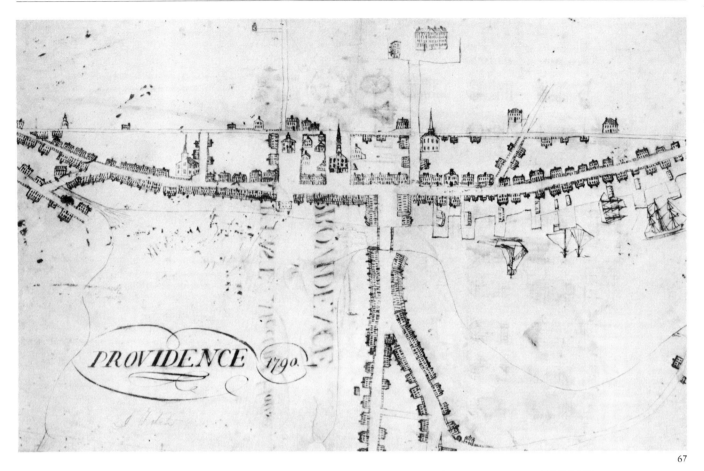

67

67

Providence 1790

John Fitch (1770–1827)

Rhode Island, 1790
Manuscript, ink; 7⅝ × 11 in.
Scale 1:7,000

Rhode Island Historical Society

Like the James Wadsworth map of New Haven (65), *Providence 1790* was drawn by a young man just graduated or on the eve of his graduation from college — in part perhaps, as an early exercise in antiquarianism or nostalgia, but also as a rite of passage. John Fitch's sketch map has no measured elements. It has major inaccuracies like the angle of intersection of Main Street and College Street. Nevertheless, the location, size, and architectural details of most of the buildings standing in the town in 1790 are all correctly rendered. These include the 1770 College Edifice, the 1775 Baptist Meeting House, the First Congregational Church, and the Beneficent Congregational Church, as well as the homes of leading Providence residents such as John Brown. The reverse of this unusual document has a pen-and-ink side elevation, also

by Fitch, of the 1775 Baptist meeting-house in Providence. The ink has bled through and is visible on the map side.

Beyond its importance as an architectural document, the Fitch map reveals that in the late eighteenth century the cartographic literacy of even an educated New Englander was still rudimentary. Despite important cartographic advances made in the eighteenth century, and despite the evolution of an American mapping technology, the naive concepts that had characterized folk or vernacular mapping for centuries — buildings shown as elevations from the street; buildings seen in three-quarter bird's-eye views; pictographic ships lying on their side in the water — were firmly embedded in the popular New England mind and were to remain so for another fifty years or more.

Born in Hopkinton, Massachusetts, in 1770, John Fitch received a degree from Rhode Island College (later Brown University) in 1790 and was ordained a Congregational minister in Danville, Vermont, in 1793. After traveling in the west, he returned to New England to serve as the minister of Guildhall, Vermont, from 1818 to 1827.

References: Historical Catalogue, 76;
Cady.

67 DETAIL illustrated p. vi.

68

[Portion of the Merrimack River between Salisbury and Newbury]

Unknown draftsman

Massachusetts, eighteenth century
Manuscript, ink and watercolor; 12 × 7⅛ in. (sight)
Scale 1:10,000

Historical Society of Old Newbury

This untitled ink-and-watercolor sketch map illustrates a portion of the Merrimack River between the present-day Massachusetts towns of Salisbury, Amesbury, and Newburyport.

Because it identifies crossings, landings, rocks, and wharves (but not soundings), it may be a fragment of a larger map designed to help owners of shallow-draft boats to find their way around the lower part of the river. Presumably, a cutout portion was preserved, colored, and framed as a relic. The detail of its land features (paths, wooded thickets, roads, and architecture), on the other hand, suggest it may have been a memory map conceived for purely decorative purposes and to preserve the location of the outstanding landmarks and navigation points along this portion of the river.

At the top right, opposite the Salisbury ferry, is the first meetinghouse of the west parish in Salisbury, fifty-two by thirty-eight feet in dimension, built 1716. The meetinghouse is one of four yellow buildings on the map, a color consistent with known meetinghouse colors in this section of Massachusetts and southern New Hampshire after 1770. This building was torn down in 1785 and replaced with the present Rocky Hill meetinghouse. A barn with three loft windows stands behind the house at Brown's landing.

References: Pettingell.

69*

List of the Inhabitants in South Windsor Street about the year 1800

John Warner Barber (1798–1885) and Abner Reed (1771–1866)
Connecticut, circa 1840
Manuscript, ink; 18⅛ × 10½ in.
Scale 1:20,000
Wood Memorial Library

Like Ezra Stiles before him (66), John Warner Barber of New Haven was an antiquarian and historian whose curiosity about all aspects of New England's topographical and local history led to a lifelong interest in maps. Beginning his career as a professional engraver in New Haven, Barber wrote and published a series of historical works based on his travels and personal observations of American antiquities. *List of the Inhabitants in South Windsor Street about the year 1800* is a memory map prepared by Barber with the assistance of the Hartford engraver Abner Reed, who, like Barber, was a native of the first or so-called south society in East Windsor, Connecticut. It was drawn by Barber sometime after the conclusion of his apprenticeship under Reed from 1813 to 1819 and after his removal to New Haven in 1823. The

map consists of a single street bounded on the north by the Scantic River and on the south by the East Hartford line. The locations of homes are shown by small squares, and the names of the owners are written beside each square. Abner Reed's home is approximately in the center; the usual tavern is found adjacent to the meetinghouse.

Barber's title is as revealing as his map. South Windsor *Street* illustrates an almost pure form of a town plan that was fairly common in New England but that in the Connecticut River Valley attained a simplicity and clarity of definition that was seldom encountered elsewhere. As in Hadley and Hatfield (26), the street runs on a north-south axis exactly parallel to the "Great River"; even the meetinghouse, like those in Hadley and Hatfield, is located in the center of the public right-of-way. Of particular interest are the clusters of identical surnames that appear on both sides of the street — a function of the common practice by which the original proprietors and landowners subdivided their shares among their sons.

References: DAB, 1:589; O'Brien; More; Linton; Stiles, Henry.

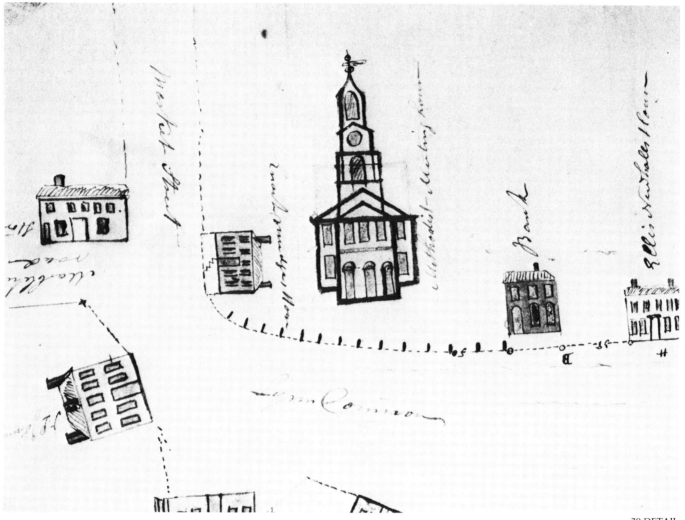

70 DETAIL

70

Lynn Common

Unknown draftsman

Massachusetts, circa 1827

Manuscript, ink and watercolor; 12½ ×
   15⅝ in.

Scale 1:600

Essex Institute

Rarely is a town center shown with
the architectural detail found on this
watercolor manuscript map of the
eastern end of Lynn Common. The
history of many of the buildings can
be traced with some success and allows a fairly accurate dating of the
map between 1825 and 1829. The
Methodist meetinghouse, built in
1812 to replace a 1791 structure that
had been the first Methodist meetinghouse in Massachusetts, is shown in
yellow paint after its steeple was lowered sixteen feet in 1824. Its rounded
pediments, facade porch, and bell
tower are rendered with accuracy. Its
pastor, Enoch Mudge, noted for writing poetry that was "rather instruc-

tive and admonitory than pleasing,"
lived next door. The known deaths of
two property owners provide a ter-
minal date for the document: J. L.
Johnson in 1829, aged sixty-three; and
Jacob Chase in 1830, aged twenty-six.
   The purpose of this document is
obscure, but it may have been prepared in connection with voting on or
planning improvements to the town
common. Executed and colored in the
naive style of a memory map, it
shows all buildings as front elevations "laid down" on a plan in a direction away from the common. The
plan is drawn to scale and cites the
distances between several houses
fronting the south road, the distance
between the schoolhouse and the
north road, and the width of the common at its east end. The schoolhouse
is shown standing on public property
at the junction of the "North," "Center," and "South" roads. A public
"Necessary" (an eighteenth- and early
nineteenth-century term for privy) is
shown as a small, two-door structure
on the west side of the county road
leading to Salem Turnpike. It is one

of the earliest known illustrations of
such conveniences in New England.

References: Lewis, *Map;* Pickles, 145;
Lewis, *History,* 205–6; Clark, 14–17; Murray, s.v. "Necessary."

71

The Map of Kensington

Thomas Rand, Jr. (1802–1866)

New Hampshire, 1823

Manuscript, ink and watercolor; 16¾ × 21¾ in.

Scale 1:16,000

New Hampshire Historical Society

The Map of Kensington by Thomas Rand, Jr., prepared at the request of the town's selectmen, shows the principal roads, mills, meeting-houses, stores, and dwelling houses of Kensington, New Hampshire, as they were found in 1823. A brilliantly colored, detailed piece of work, the map lists the owners of 113 dwelling houses, each shown in elevation as it would be seen from the nearest road. (The Greek Revival had not yet made itself evident — no gable ends face the street.) Some architectural distinctions are made: twenty-four dwelling houses are one-story cottages, usually with only one or two windows; five dwelling houses are substantial homes with as many as nine windows. While stereotyped,

Rand's architectural renderings are accurate in at least some instances. A house in Eastman's Corner owned by the "Heirs of Dr. Page" is shown as a principal dwelling with an attached ell. A Kensington history confirms the existence of this ell by noting that it was detached sometime after 1823 and moved to the back of the lot.

Dominating the map is the 1771 Congregational meetinghouse shown in three-quarter elevation. Patterned after the North Hill meetinghouse in nearby North Hampton, the Kensington meetinghouse in turn served as the model for the meetinghouse in Salisbury. Half-rounded, pedimented doorways are visible on the south and east sides; the orange doors, light yellow clapboards, and Spanish-brown roof are consistent with other known color combinations of the period. A short distance away stands the "Baptist Meeting House." This denomination probably had only a brief history in the town since it is not mentioned in the several town histories of Kensington.

Rand's map reveals the stability of eighteenth- and early nineteenth-century New England society. Although

the ownership of the 113 homes is distributed among fifty-four different surnames, eight surnames — all of them families present in the town at its incorporation in 1732 — account for about one-half of them. The major unanswered question is why Thomas Rand hand-colored his memory map of Kensington, adding a crude but detailed *trompe l'oeil* framing. Perhaps he was paid extra to draw these flourishes. Town maps were a local genre in this section of New Hampshire and were appreciated by the same families who purchased and enjoyed Phinehas Merrill's engraved maps of Stratham and Exeter (44–47).

References: Sawyer, 253, 289–367; Dow, 931; Parsons, 66–67, 209, 499–512; Kensington.

71 DETAIL

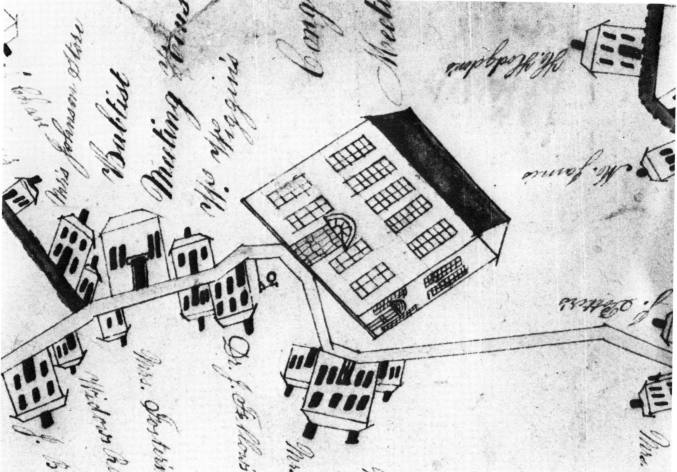

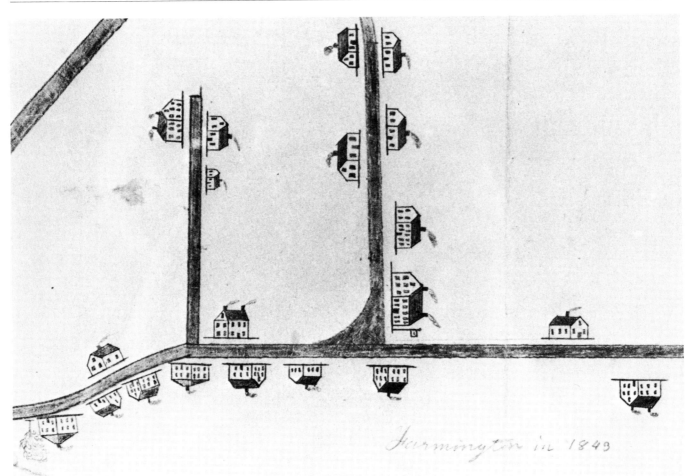

Farmington in 1849

72 DETAIL

72

Farmington in 1843

Unknown draftsman

New Hampshire, circa 1851
Manuscript, pencil; 16½ × 13⅝ in.
Scale 1:5,000

New Hampshire Historical Society

73

Farmington in Jan 1851

Unknown draftsman

New Hampshire, 1851
Manuscript, pencil; 16½ × 13¾ in.
Scale 1:5,000

New Hampshire Historical Society

The Cocheco link of the Dover-to-Rochester railway was first chartered in 1847; ground for the railroad was broken in July 1848. Two pencil maps of Farmington, New Hampshire, drawn by an unknown artist in 1851 record the sudden growth of the town following the completion of the Cocheco link in September 1849. (Fifty-six new structures were built between 1843 and 1851 in an area of approximately one square mile.) This growth took place at a time when the agricultural populations of rural New Hampshire communities were being depleted by the continuing westward migration of farmers, and towns were economically and demographically booming or failing according to the routes selected by the railroad companies.

Both maps illustrate the survival of naive cartography in nineteenth-century rural New England. Houses are shown fully laid down or three-quarters laid down. Rivers, roads, railroads, wells, and smoking chimneys are shown as simple features on a two-dimensional landscape. Since both maps are drawn on identical blue paper, it is presumed that both were done at the same time and that

the 1843 version is a memory map. Their purpose may in part have been antiquarian or nostalgic, looking back to the uncluttered appearance of the town before the arrival of the railroad. On the other hand, the maps may have been drawn as an expression of pride to show how quickly the town had grown. The area depicted in both maps is located at the junction of the Ela and Cocheco rivers in the northern part of the town. Farmington lies in the Winnipesaukee region of New Hampshire, near the Maine border.

References: McDuffie, 2: 490–93.

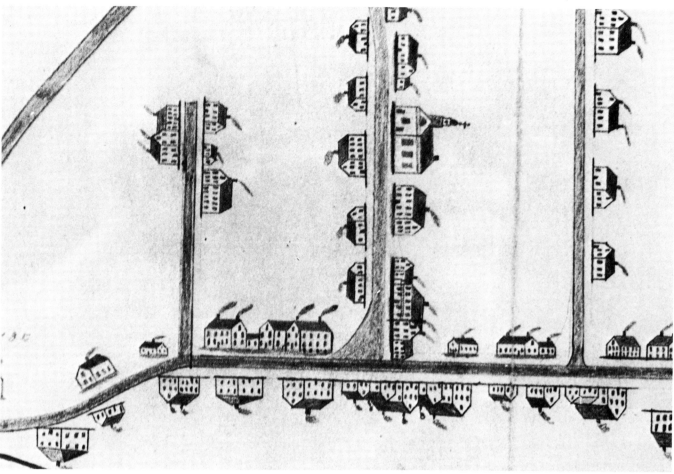

73 DETAIL

74

Chronicles of the Frost Family

Elias Frost (1782–1863)

New Hampshire, 1852 (Meriden Parish)

Bound manuscript volume, ink; 6¾ × 4½ in. (closed)

Dartmouth College Library

Dr. Elias Frost's *Outline of Meriden Center as it was in 1808* is one of seven memory maps sketched into the opening pages of a family narrative written by him in 1853 titled *Chronicles of the Frost Family*. These memory maps depict the principal landmarks of the three most important neighborhoods Frost knew in his youth and early adulthood. These neighborhoods were Milford, Massachusetts, where he lived with his father, the Reverend Amariah Frost, until the latter's death in 1792; Uxbridge, Massachusetts, where he lived and studied for the medical profession in the household of his guardian, Dr. Samuel Willard; and Meriden parish in Plainfield, New Hampshire, where he began his medical practice in 1808 four years after his graduation from Brown Univer-

sity. As he explains in a note accompanying his chronicle, Dr. Frost drew his maps to "enable the reader to better understand many of the circumstances" in his narrative. As he noted, the outlines were "very imperfect as to the shape of the buildings," but, he added,

> they are correct as to size or either one or two story houses. The meeting houses, Rev A Frosts house, Doct. Willards house, John Caprons house, the Tavern of Peter White, The School Houses and the shape of the commons are as correct as I will describe them, also Hon Daniel Kimballs house, stores, sheds, meeting house & school house with their several situations are as correct as I could remember they were.

Certain key topographical and architectural features recur in all seven maps, including meetinghouses with their accompanying horse sheds, schoolhouses, burying grounds, taverns, mills, bridges, commons, and roads. Appropriately, those houses and grounds that play the most prominent role in his narrative — the houses of his father, of his guardian, and of the judge (Hon. Daniel Kimball) at whose home he boarded when he first moved to Meriden — are drawn with the most detail. Rendered

particularly closely are the Willard gardens and grounds in Uxbridge, which are divided into upper, middle, and lower "squares"; a "back yard"; a "Plow and corn field"; an "orchard"; and a "Lane to Pasture" leading to the pond and bridge.

Dr. Frost wrote his chronicle at the age of seventy-one, five years after an operation for cataracts in his eyes caused him to give up his practice. He was remembering locations of buildings and landscape features as they existed fifty to sixty years earlier, without the benefit of measured distances. Although his maps appear at first glance to be compact town centers, the houses shown on them are separated by as much as three or more miles. Like so many untrained mapmakers, Frost "laid down" his houses, though in some instances they are shown in bird's-eye perspective.

References: Frost, 200–202; Meriden.

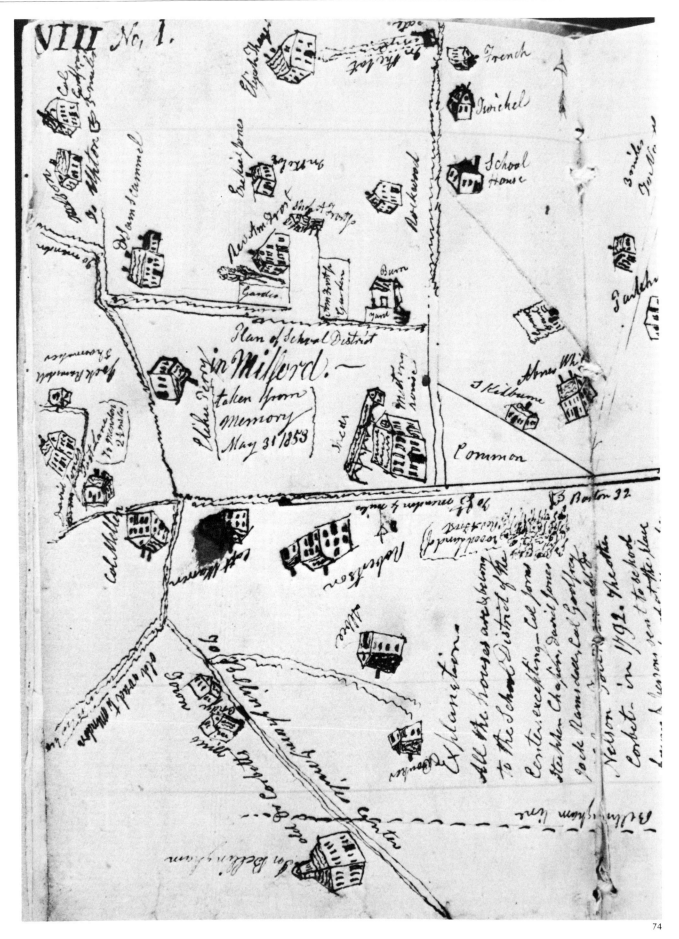

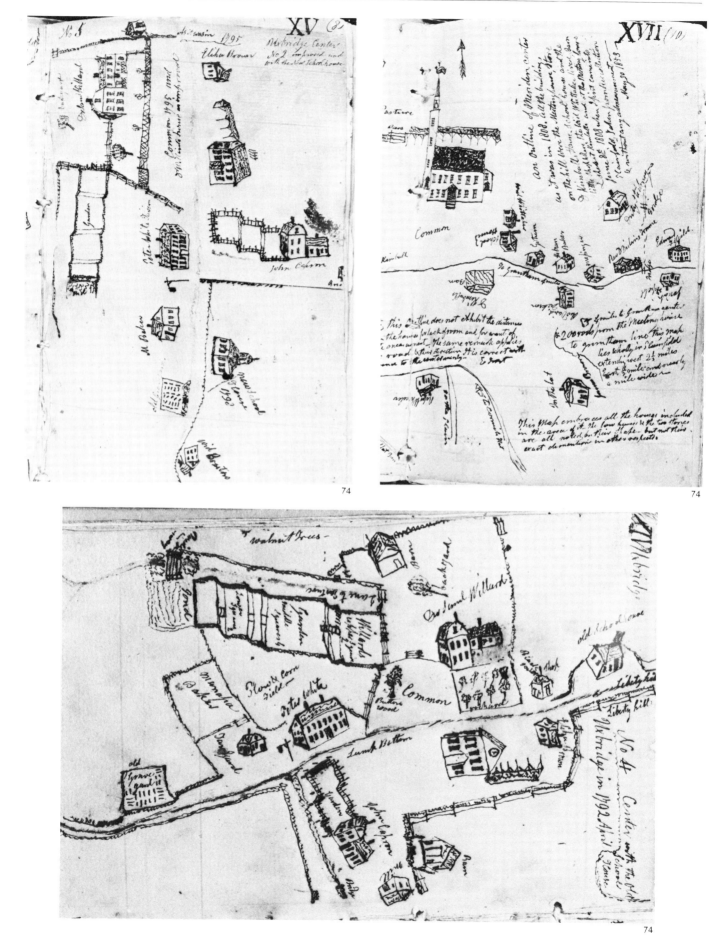

75 *

Mr. John Allen of Dedham his ffarme Layd out at Bogganistoe

Justin Noyes

Massachusetts, 1649
Manuscript, ink; 17 × 12 in.
Scale 1:3,200
Massachusetts Archives

76 *

Layd out unto the Hon.d Gov.r Jn.o Endecott Esqr. 550 acres of land, on Ipswich River

Thomas Danforth (1622–1699) and Robert Hale

Massachusetts, 1659 (Ipswich)
Manuscript, ink and applied pastel; 10¼ × 8¼ in.
Scale 1:13,000
Massachusetts Archives

So long as large tracts of land remained unincorporated in New England, seventeenth-century colonial and provincial governments reserved the right to make direct grants to individual petitioners or to reward the services of magistrates and soldiers who had served the body politic. The earliest cartographic document in the Massachusetts Archives is a confirmation of a grant of land on the west bank of the Charles River near Med-

field given to John Allen by the General Court of the Massachusetts Bay Colony in the mid-seventeenth century. Believed to be the work of surveyor Justin Noyes, *Mr. John Allen of Dedham his ffarme Layd out at Bogganistoe* was approved by the court 17 May 1649. It depicts 200 acres in what is now the town of Millis near the southern bounds of Sherborn enclosing the present South End Pond. Hachured lines designate the swamp of wetlands around the pond and brook. Pictographic hardwoods and pines indicate the area suitable for pasturage and cultivation. John Allen (or Allin) was the first minister of Dedham, Massachusetts. He held a reputation as one of the "largest landholders" in Dedham, in part the consequence of grants made to him by the Colony and the town of Dedham. The name "Bogganistoe" survives as Boggastowe Brook and Pond in Millis.

A tract of land more than double the size given to Allen was granted by the Colony General Court to John Endecott in 1659. Thomas Danforth and Robert Hale's survey, *Layd out unto the Hon.d Gov.r Jn.o Endecott Esqr. 550 acres of land, on Ipswich River*, whose original at the Massachusetts Archives is colored a brilliant green, confirmed a grant that

Endecott had received in 1639 but that had never been measured. Like John Winthrop and Thomas Dudley, Endecott had selected the tract personally, all three having given themselves 1,000- and 500-acre parcels of land for their service as governors of the colony. On learning of the existence of copper ore deposits on his property, Endecott purchased 1,000 additional acres on the Ipswich River in 1657 and insisted that the Court confirm the original property to him. Located at the "Blinde Hole" region on the Ipswich River, the copper ore was extracted by "Mr. Leader." Endecott and the Colony fell out with Leader when the project failed.

Elected an Assistant to the Colony the same year he surveyed Endecott's property, Thomas Danforth later served as Deputy Governor of Massachusetts and as a justice in the witchcraft trials of 1692. The surveyor Robert Hale has not been identified.

References: Danforth and Danforth, 4–7; Endicott, 84; Mayo, 130–31, 282–83; Chapple; Lamson, 29, 87–89.

77

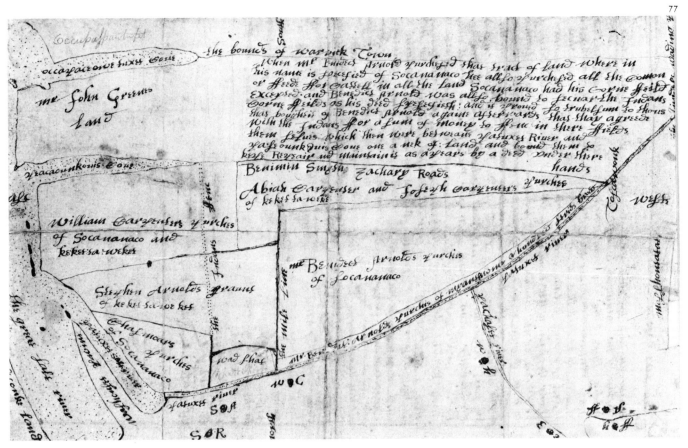

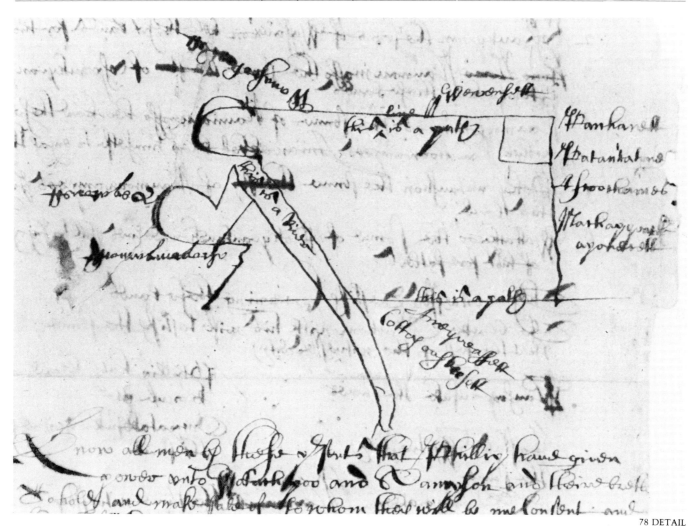

78 DETAIL

77

. . . that tract of land where in his name is specefied . . .

Unknown draftsman

Rhode Island, 1 March 1661 (Pawtuxet)
Manuscript, ink; 8⅜ × 12¾ in.
Scale 1:30,000
Rhode Island Historical Society

This document, one of the few of its type to survive, records a 1661 agreement absolving the English owners of land in Pawtuxet, Rhode Island, from maintaining fences that protected Indian cornfields from English cattle. (The fence line in question is indicated by two stippled lines and extends one and a half miles between Peacacunkonis Cove and the Pawtuxet River.) The issue began twenty-three years earlier in 1638 when William Arnold and his son Benedict purchased from the Narragansett sachem Socananaco rights to grazing and common lands that contained cornfields kept by Socananaco and that required protection from English an-imals. Under the terms of the initial purchase, Benedict Arnold was to build and maintain a fence to protect Socananaco's fields, an obligation that was passed to new owners when Benedict Arnold sold portions of his land to other English settlers. However, as noted in the 1661 agreement, the obligation

> proved so trubelsum to those that bought of Benedict Arnold that they agreede with the Indians for a sum of money to fence in their ffield themselves.

The Pawtuxet difficulties were not an isolated case: fencing agreements were made by the Plymouth Colony with the Nauset Indians in 1644. The records of this colony for the year 1671 indicate the government had to appoint committees in no fewer than eleven towns in its jurisdiction "to view the Damage done to the Indians by the Horses and Hoggs of the English."

References: Adams, James, 344; Fuller, 53; Baylies, 1:219; *Map showing the Pawtuxet Lands.*

78

. . . the prinsipall names of the land we are now willing should be sold

John Sassamon (?) (d. 1675)

Plymouth Colony, 1666
Seventeenth-century manuscript copy of deed document signed by King Philip; bound in "Indian Deeds. Treasurer Accounts; Lists of Freemen" I:21; 10½ × 6¾ in.

Plymouth County Commissioners

Shortly after he inherited leadership of the Wampanoag tribe from his late half brother Alexander, King Philip, the son of Massasoit, began to sell off portions of his territory to the land-hungry English who were penetrating traditional Wampanoag tribal lands in southeastern Massachusetts. *The prinsipall names of the land we are now willing should be sold*, a seventeenth-century clerk's copy of a 1666 land deed signed by Philip, which was subsequently redated 1668, gave exclusive authorization to two lesser sachems, Watashpoo and

Sampson, to sell lands within the area described on the map. The difficulty of correctly transcribing the seventeenth-century script, coupled with the apparent lack of place-name survivals, makes it hard to pinpoint the precise location of the area specified in this deed. It most likely represents the shoreline of the present towns of Rochester, Marion, and Mattapoisett in Bristol County, Massachusetts. North is probably at the right. If this hypothesis is accurate, at least one place name has survived. It can be read as Sepaconett on the map and identifies a peninsula in Mattapoisett now called Sepaconit.

The terms of the deed are as revealing as the sketch map itself. First is the condition that "the Indians that are upon it may live upon it still" — evidence pointing to the lack of a land-tenure tradition within the Algonquian culture. Second is Philip's manner of describing the area he was "now willing should be sold." Rather than indicating a cohesive boundary, he cited "all the prinsipall names of the land," in effect creating a toponymic map in which names are shown in relationship to one another and to geographical features so familiar as not to require naming (for example, "River"). This suggests that a rich and highly descriptive oral legacy of geographical place names existed in the Algonquian tradition at the time of the European migrations and settlements of the early seventeenth century. Equally important, it reveals an almost complete lack of a cartographic or abstract literacy in Algonquian culture. Ultimately, this is an English document, conceived, written, and illustrated for English purposes and from an English point of view. The document was witnessed by King Philip's secretary, the Harvard-educated Wampanoag John Sassamon, who also probably drew the map.

References: "Topography," 267; Barber, *Massachusetts,* 256; Ryder, 22; Leonard, 7.

79

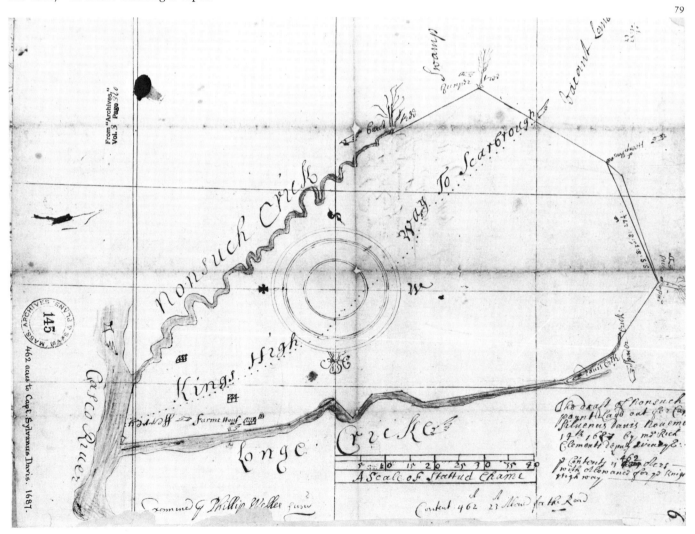

79

The draft of Nonsuch poynt Layd out for Cap.! Silvenus Davis . . .

Richard Clements

District of Maine, 1687 (Falmouth)
Manuscript, ink; signed by Richard Clements and examined by Phillip Wells; 12 × 15½ in.
Scale 1:7,000

Massachusetts Archives

80 *

Lif.ᵗ Cor.!ⁱⁱ Nicolas Paige his Little farme Lif.ᵗ Cor.!ⁱⁱ Nicolas Paige his great farme

Phillip Wells

Massachusetts, 1687 (Chelsea)
Manuscript, ink; 14 × 12 in.
Scale 1:8,000

Massachusetts Archives

The intense unpopularity of James II's appointment of Joseph Dudley and Edmund Andros as Governors of the Dominion of New England from 1685 to 1688 went beyond the introduction of episcopacy into Boston and the suspension of the Massachusetts Charter. Equally resented was the order declaring that property titles previously negotiated under Massachusetts Bay colony laws were no longer in force and that all patents and titles had to be renegotiated — in effect giving Andros and his supporters wide latitude in determining who owned property and in coercing fees as quit-rents. Not surprisingly, therefore, the years of the Dominion saw numerous lot surveys made of properties in dispute between rightful owners and individuals with close ties to Andros.

Prominent among the land measurers active at this time was Phillip Wells (50), who as Surveyor General under Edmund Andros was sought by Andros supporters who were involved in litigation. Lieutenant Colonel Nicholas Paige, a member of the Church of England and a declared enemy of pro-Charter Puritan interests, had long contested the ownership of two farms in Rumney Marsh inherited from his father-in-law, Robert Keayne. He took advantage of the deteriorating political position of Elisha Cooke, who occupied the farms, to initiate in 1684 legal proceedings for their recovery — a suit that succeeded with the arrival of Andros in Boston. *Lif.ᵗ Cor.!ⁱⁱ Nicholas Paige his Little farme . . . his great farme* by Phillip Wells was probably ordered by Paige after he took over the contested property in 1687 and wished to know its bounds. Abutting what is now the Pines River between Saugus and Re-

vere, his "great farme" was about one mile square; his "Little farme," about a quarter of that size. Wells drew on the map two clusters of farm buildings shown in perspective, and he differentiated between "Meadows," "Pastur Land," and enclosed cultivated land behind the farm buildings. Elisha Cooke countersued after 1700, and the case came before Judge Samuel Sewall. But Paige retained possession of the farms and willed them at his death in 1717 to his niece Martha (Hobbs) Oliver whose husband, Captain Nathaniel Oliver, was listed as the owner in 1739.

(Phillip Wells was also involved in the usurpation of Clark's Island in Plymouth Harbor, jointly owned by the towns of Plymouth and Duxbury and set aside for the support of the poor of Duxbury. Under a "Warrant" from Andros, Wells ran a survey of the island in 1687 on behalf of Nathaniell Clarke who was then serving on Andros's Council and who was given title to the island by Andros. When the Duxbury minister Ichabod Wiswall protested this, he was summoned to Boston and fined four pounds.)

Governor Andros's Deputy Surveyor, Richard Clements, was similarly employed by parties close to Andros. *The draft of Nonsuch poynt Layd out for Cap.! Silvenus Davis,* prepared by Clements and "Examined by Phillip Welles, Surveyor," recorded a tract of land on the Casco River that was owned by a Falmouth resident who cooperated with Andros, and who, together with a member of Andros's Council, Edward Tyng, persuaded a number of Falmouth residents to run surveys and pay exorbitant fees for the confirmation of their deeds. This aroused the opposition of residents who refused to pay these fees, among them Robert Lawrence, whose property abutted Davis's on Cleeves' Neck. Clements's plan depicts the "Kings Highway" to Scarborough, a "farme House," and outbuildings. Falmouth was captured and destroyed by French and Indian forces in 1690, and Robert Lawrence lost his life. Sylvanus Davis, imprisoned by the French, was redeemed and spent his remaining years in Boston. Richard Clements, who prepared twenty-three surveys now in the Massachusetts Archives dated 1687 and 1688, later became a warrant officer aboard the H.M.S. *Nonesuch.*

References: Palfrey, 2:325–27; Bradford, 1:174–75; Willis, 231, 257–69, 284–85, 293, map; Mass. Archives, Clements; Chamberlain, 1: 656–62, map; 2:1–17.

81

A Platt of Land in Dorchester Woods . . .

Joshua Fisher (1610–1672)

Massachusetts, circa 1670
Manuscript, ink; 16¼ × 13½ in.
Scale 1:9,500

Boston Public Library

A Platt of Land in Dorchester Woods, computed and drawn by the Dedham surveyor Joshua Fisher (34), records the division of 500 acres of common land among the sixty proprietary shareholders of the town of Dorchester about the year 1670. The area shown occupies what is now the Hyde Park sector of Dorchester at the junction of Mother Brook and the Neponset River. Following what was an accepted seventeenth-century practice, the largest lots were assigned to the principal shareholders or to the proprietors with the largest estates. Among these were William Stoughton, a benefactor of Harvard College, Governor of the Massachusetts Bay Colony, and a presiding judge at the witchcraft trials; and Major Humphrey Atherton, whose grave slab is one of the earliest markers at the Dorchester North Burial Ground. The division reserved a number of acres "for the Poor of Dorchester for firewood." One lot was assigned to the Dorchester church.

Joshua Fisher's use of "long lots" is probably a combination of two factors. First is the relative simplicity of running parallel lines. More important, however, is the transference of open-field lot division practices in England to solve land distribution and measurement needs in New England.

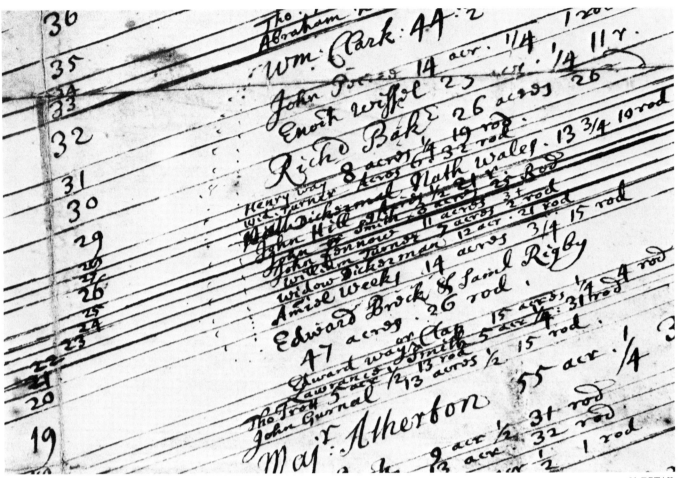

81 DETAIL

In order to reduce the number of turn-abouts made by a plowman and his team, English open-field cultivation rights were assigned in narrow strips of furlong length (220 yards). Joshua Fisher, who emigrated from Syleham, Suffolk County, England, to Dorchester at about the age of twenty was undoubtedly familiar with this method of lot division and applied it, as did other surveyors, to the division of "rights" or "shares." In most instances, proprietary lot lines such as these made no lasting impression on the landscape. In this instance, however, the alignment of at least some streets in present-day Hyde Park (Cleveland, Winslow, Town) appears to conform to the division lines in Fisher's lots; and present-day Church Street remains a toponymic survival on the exact location of Fisher's "church lot." A later hand (probably writing 1670–1690) listed those lots whose owners had changed.

References: Dorchester, 185; Fisher; Jenney; Richeson, 16–17.

82

... the WAY Petition'd for ...

Unknown draftsman

Massachusetts, 1717 (Ipswich)
Manuscript, ink; 12¾ × 16⅝ in.
Scale 1:2,500

Essex Institute

83

... the foot way now in Contest

Unknown draftsman

Massachusetts, 1717 (Ipswich)
Manuscript, ink; 17 × 13¼ in.
Scale 1:4,000

Essex Institute

Two of the most conceptually powerful maps that have survived from New England's early history were drawn in connection with a right-of-way controversy involving the property of Beamsley Perkins of Ipswich, Massachusetts. The controversy began in 1710 when Perkins acquired ownership of five and a half acres of land that were crossed by a pathway used as a shortcut from Scot's Lane to the Ipswich meetinghouse. Wishing to discourage public use of his new property, Perkins fenced off the pathway, planted an orchard in it, and removed the squared logs that served as a bridge over a small brook. In 1717 a number of Ipswich residents who had been accustomed to using the footpath responded with a petition to the local court claiming they were being unfairly "molested" by Perkins, who denied them their traditional or "Ancient" rights. The WAY Petition'd for and the foot way now in Contest were prepared when the case came before the magistrates. Both maps are freehand sketches showing lot boundaries as taken from "Grants on Record" (property deeds). Houses are shown in elevation and labeled with past and current owners. The half-mile footway can be seen following the edges of property lines so as to cause the least inconvenience to the owners. The letters A and B identify the thirty-rod section of the footway that traversed Perkins's land. The architectural details have a calligraphic or "copied" style, presumably because the maps were hastily made duplicates several times removed from the original. A number of important features nevertheless emerge: for example, the arched side

78

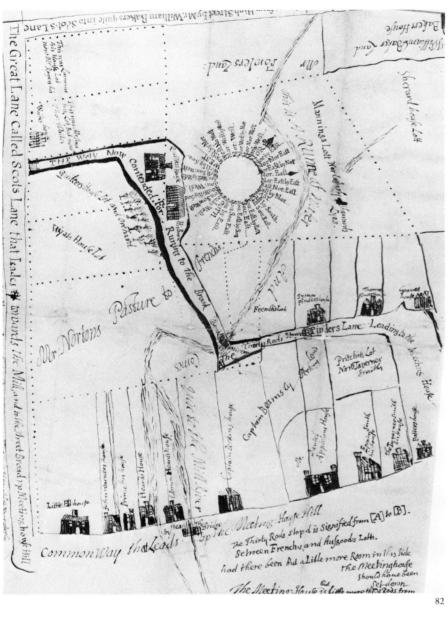

entry to Quillers Barn and the gabled roof and flag-vane of the 1700 Ipswich meetinghouse. At least five dwelling houses have prominent gables. Single-cell, side-chimney dwellings can be distinguished from two-cell dwellings with a central chimney. "Mr. Daniel Appletons House" has a chimney at each end.

Although both maps appear to be by the same hand, small but important differences between them confuse their relationship to one another and their role in the controversy. Three houses that appear on *the WAY* version (Heard's House, Waite's house, and Epraim Smith's house) do not appear on *the foot way* version; additionally, the "Runne of water" that enters into the controversy appears only on *the WAY*. This suggests that the larger-scale *WAY* version may have been designed to show features not clearly set forth in *the foot way*. It also suggests that a number of years may have elapsed between the preparation of *the foot way* and *the WAY*, allowing time for the construction of three new dwelling houses.

Captain Beamsley Perkins accompanied the third English expedition against Port Royal in 1719 and was listed as owner of the brig *Ipswich* in 1714. He had a local reputation for carrying matters "with a high hand," and his marriage (made without publishments) to Hannah Glasier of Ipswich by the minister John Emerson in 1697 caused the loss of Emerson's legal right to join couples. The disposition of the residents' case against Perkins is not known.

82

References: Waters, Thomas F., 2:339, 342–52.

83 illustrated p. xiv.

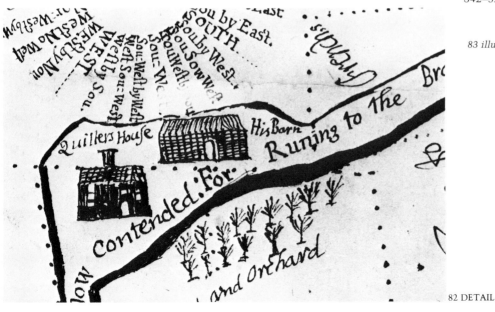

82 DETAIL

84

This is a Draft of Cap.! Henry Bull's Lots Lying in South Kingstown . . .

James Helme (1710–1777)

Rhode Island, 1729 (South Kingston)
Manuscript, ink and watercolor; 11⅞ × 14⅝ in.

Scale 1:7,000

Rhode Island Historical Society

The grandson of one of the founders and seventeenth-century governors of Rhode Island, Captain Henry Bull was a resident of Newport and for many years a Deputy and Speaker to the Rhode Island General Assembly. Among his properties were two lots in South Kingstown, in what was called the Pettaquamscutt Purchase, at one time owned by William Bundy but later occupied by Jireh Bull. In 1729, Captain Henry Bull, who probably inherited the property from a relative, commissioned James Helme to measure the two lots "as the fences now stand." Helme's *Draft of Cap.! Henry Bull's Lots Lying in South Kingstown* shows that the lots lay on both sides of a "highway," later to become the Boston Post Road and now U.S. Route 1. A house and orchard stand near the road on the larger of the two lots.

In 1917 Helme's map led to the successful location and subsequent archeological investigation of the Jireh Bull garrison house whose destruction by Narragansetts in December 1675 was recorded by William Hubbard in his *History of the Indian Wars* (see 9):

> The next day Captain Prentice with his troop being sent to Pettyquamcot: returned with sad news of burning Jerry Bull's garrison house . . . and killing 10 Englishmen and 5 women and children but two escaped in all. This is the chance of war which they who undertake must prepare to undergo.

Shown as the "Old Garison" on the *Draft*, the site had been a ruin already for fifty-four years when Helme recorded its location. Two hundred years later it was an unrecognizable cluster of mounds.

The surveyor James Helme was a son of Rouse Helme, Judge of the Rhode Island Superior Court for twenty years. Helme was commissioned by the Rhode Island Assembly to copy all the South Kingston Records. He collaborated with William Chandler to survey and chart the boundaries of Rhode Island after they were fixed in 1741.

References: Isham: Monahon; Chapin, *Check List*, 8–9.

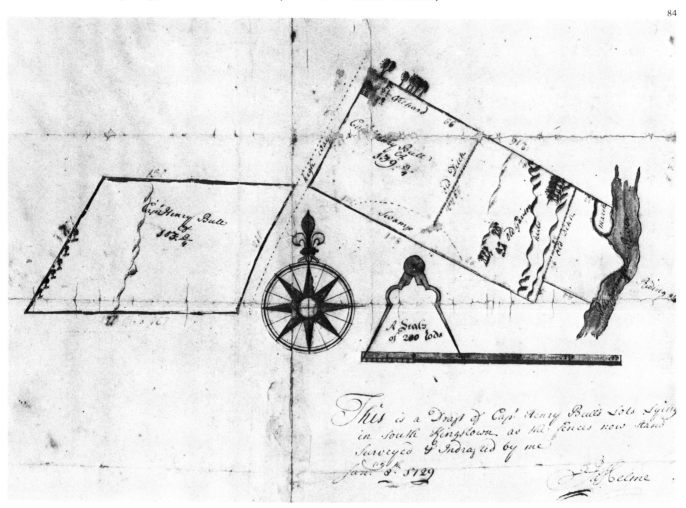

84

85

. . . The Estate of William Thompson Esquire 1753

Thomas Barnes

Massachusetts, 1753 (Chelsea)
Manuscript, ink and watercolor; 26 × 33 in. (sight)
Scale 1:5,000

The Henry Whitfield House

The English-style "estate map," a property plan whose purpose was both decorative and administrative, did not become an accepted mapping form in New England where small holdings were the rule and tenancies on large properties the exception. In some instances, however, estate maps of properties held by absentee English owners have survived. *The Estate of William Thompson Esquire 1753* by Thomas Barnes depicts a seventy-eight-acre eighteenth-century New England farm located in what is now the southern portion of Chelsea, Massachusetts, just across from East Boston (formerly Noddles Island). Gates, stiles, wells, and ponds are marked with appropriate symbols. Apple trees line the principal fields and pastures. The farmhouse, with its wing, is located at the head of the "causey" (causeway) to Noddles Island.

The elaborate cartouches, arms, and other technical and toponymic details identify this map as the work of an English cartographer. For example, the trees, shown in three-quarter perspective, have a carefully executed shadow. Terms such as "Close" (enclosure), "walk" (pasture), "Ing" or "Ying" (wetland meadow), and "coppice" (thicket or copse) do not normally occur in New England land nomenclature. Barnes's "explanation" notes that all the lands are "Inclosed," a concept that would be taken for granted in New England.

Thomas Barnes prepared the map in England on the basis of information supplied to him by tenants of the farm. William Thompson of Suffolk is believed to have been a relative of Robert Thompson of England, who purchased the Whitfield House in Guilford, Connecticut, after the death of Henry Whitfield in 1657. The map was given to the Whitfield House Museum in 1932 by an English donor. According to Mellen Chamberlain's *Documentary History of Chelsea,* a member of the Eustace family of Chelsea occupied Thompson's estate in 1739.

References: Chamberlain, 1:map; Murray, s.v. "ing."

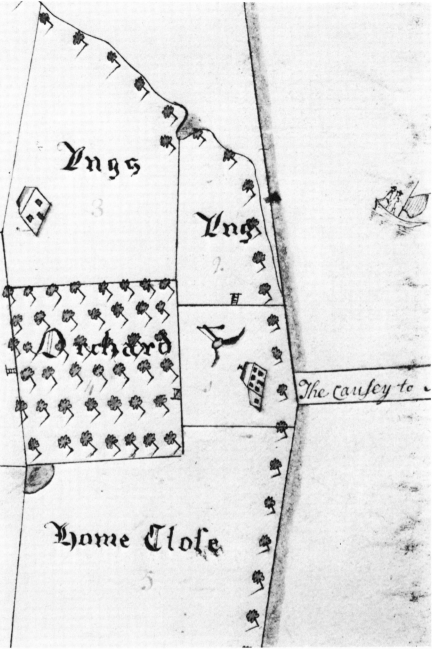

85 DETAIL

86*

The Plan of Holderness

Abraham Bachelder (circa 1725–1805?)

New Hampshire, 1762
Manuscript, ink; 35 × 14⅛ in.
Scale 1:12,000

New Hampshire Historical Society

Holderness was first chartered as a township in 1751 to a group of proprietors from Durham, New Hampshire. Because of delays occasioned by the French and Indian War (1756–1760), the 1751 charter expired and Governor Benning Wentworth rechartered the town in 1761 to the same group. *The Plan of Holderness*, drawn by Abraham Bachelder of Boscawen and Louden, New Hampshire, in 1762 surveys and records the division of home lots and intervale rights of the Pemigewasset River and on Spring Creek commissioned by the Durham proprietors after they had secured their second charter. Bachelder's plan follows the outline of an earlier one by Samuel Lane (1718–1806) of Stratham, New Hampshire, in 1751. However, Bachelder's plan consolidated among thirty shareholders the same area (approximately 500 acres) that in 1751 had been apportioned among seventy. (Governor Benning Wentworth received a choice "neck" of land located between the upper and lower intervales and marked "B.W.")

The actual topographic evolution of Holderness varied considerably from the projected lot lines and rights-of-way shown on Bachelder's map. Virtually none of the one-acre home lots became the site of farms; none of the projected range ways became roads. Instead, the settlement of the town developed around two principal highways. One, the 1763 Province Road (whose location had been determined by the New Hampshire government), followed the eastern bank of the Pemigewasset and passed to the east of the choice intervale lands of the 1762 division. The second, the 1771 College Road (financed by Benning Wentworth, who wanted a direct route to Dartmouth College from his country seat in Wolfeborough) was laid out by a committee of three on which the Holderness proprietors were represented only by the town clerk, Samuel Shepard.

References: Hodges, 12–36; Batchelder; Lane, *Plan*.

87*

Plan of the farm of land belonging to Mr. Dav.ᵈ Ogden late of Fairfield Deceasd

Gideon Welles

Connecticut, 20 April 1769
Manuscript, iron gall ink; 16¼ × 12⅞ in.
Scale 1:3,000

Fairfield Historical Society

New England estate inventory maps (91, 94) differed from English "estate maps" in that they were legal rather than decorative or administrative instruments. They were commonly prepared where property inheritances had not been confirmed at the time of the death of a landowner and had to be portioned among several heirs. A Surveyor of Land for the County of Fairfield, Connecticut, Gideon Welles was appointed to measure and divide the property of David Ogden of Fairfield, a farmer, who died March 1768 in his seventy-fourth year and whose land abutted Perry's Mill Pond between a causeway and a county road leading to Greenfield. Welles's *Plan of the farm of land belonging to Mr. Dav.ᵈ Ogden late of Fairfield Deceasd*, drawn on a scale of 16 rods to an inch, was prepared in April 1769. At the time of David Ogden's death, his sons David and Jonathan were occupying houses and barns on the property. Welles was instructed by the probate court to make a division that reflected this occupancy, while also allowing for the "Widow's Thirds." Welles's plan included side elevations of the houses occupied by David and Jonathan, both of which are still standing. The division of the father's estate was not confirmed until 8 March 1776, by which time both of the sons had died.

References: Schenck, 400–401.

88

. . . this Diagram . . . February 15th day AD 1786

Joab Griswold

Connecticut, 15 February 1786 (Simsbury)
Manuscript, ink; 36¼ × 18¾ in.
Scale 1:8,000

Yale University Library

The parishes of Turkey Hills and Salmon Brook, formed in 1726 in the wake of a bitter meetinghouse site controversy, remained thinly settled communities in the northern part of Simsbury, Connecticut, during most of the eighteenth century. When their population reached approximately twenty-five hundred, they petitioned in 1786 for incorporation as the separate town of Granby, an appeal that won approval by the Connecticut Legislature. Before agreement was reached on this separation, however, it was necessary to distribute a tract of undivided land in the southwestern part of Simsbury among the principal residents of West Simsbury and the proposed new town of Granby. Accordingly, Joab Griswold, Hartford County Surveyor, was hired to measure and mark off divisions in the so-called Second Mile Tier in Simsbury (now part of the town of Canton) just north of the Farmington town line (now Avon). Griswold's *Diagram*, signed and dated 15 February 1786, measures off sixty-six courses in a range one mile in width, each course running parallel to the "Squadron Line" at the top of the plan. The largest shares of 80 rods and 40 rods were reserved for the earliest settlers of West Simsbury and Turkey Hills (Richard Case and Joseph Phelps, Sr.). The Pettibone, Case, and Humphrey families were awarded substantial amounts. A widow and two unmarried women were also among the recipients, however.

Joab Griswold, who also did the survey of Louden, Massachusetts (37), decorated his plan with trees, houses, a snake, turkey, fox, and rabbit. These were done in the same calligraphic style as those in the Louden survey and resemble the drawings of the Godsoe family surveyors of Kittery, Maine (89–95).

References: Ellsworth, 45–51; Phelps, 170–75, 110, 136–40.

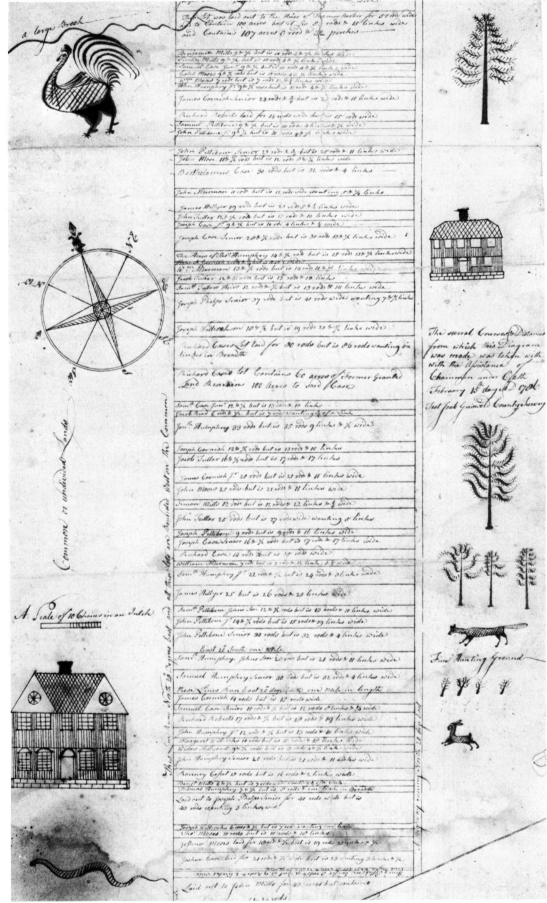

89

Elihu Gunnison's Land at Brian's Point

William Godsoe (circa 1650–1730+)

District of Maine, 5 March 1697 (Kittery)
Manuscript copy, ink, dated 1722 by Joseph Hammond, Kittery Town Clerk, of a manuscript by Godsoe; bound in Kittery Town Records; 14 × 18 in. (image)
Scale 1:3,000

Town of Kittery

90*

the Land in Controversey Claimed by m^r Christan Remick and improved By Samull Spinney

William Godsoe (circa 1650–1730+)

District of Maine, 18 December 1697 (Kittery)
Manuscript, ink and watercolor; 12⅛ × 15¾ in.
Scale 1:3,000

Maine State Archives

91

A Plott of m^r Humphrey Chadburns Farm att Sturgen Creek

William Godsoe (circa 1650–1730+)

District of Maine, 6 October 1701 (Kittery)
Manuscript, ink and watercolor; 14 × 11 in. (image)
Scale 1:3,000

Maine State Archives

92*

Elihu Gunnison . . . Plat or Mapp of his 300 acres of Land

William Godsoe (circa 1650–1730+)

District of Maine, 1713 (Kittery)
Manuscript, red and black ink; 26⅛ × 18⅛ in.
Scale 1:7,000

New Hampshire Historical Society

93

Late Major Hooke houselot lying neere Kittery Point

William Godsoe (circa 1650–1730+)

District of Maine, 29 August 1715
Manuscript copy, ink, dated 1716, by Joseph Hammond, Kittery Town Clerk, of a manuscript by Godsoe; bound in Kittery Town Records; 11 × 17 in. (image)
Scale 1:3,000

Town of Kittery

94

. . . Division of y^e Lands of m^r John Hole Late of Kittery Deceas:

John Godsoe (fl. 1736–1769)

District of Maine, 17 December 1739
Manuscript, red and black ink, and watercolor; 11⅜ × 14⅛ in.
Scale 1:3,000

New Hampshire Historical Society

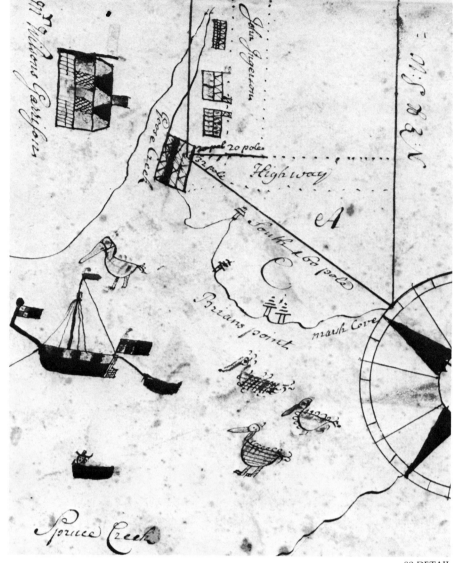

89 DETAIL

95

Division of y^e Lands of m^r John Hole Late of Kittery Deceas:

John Godsoe (fl. 1736–1769)

District of Maine, 17 December 1739
Manuscript copy, ink, dated circa 1740, by Tobias Leighton, Kittery Town Clerk, of a manuscript by Godsoe; bound in Kittery Town Records; 14 × 9 in.
Scale 1:3,000

Town of Kittery

The closest approximation to folk or vernacular mapping in New England is found in the work of an immigrant English mariner and surveyor named William Godsoe of Kittery, Maine, and his grandson John Godsoe, who were active during an eighty-year period from 1689 to 1769. Hired by Kittery landowners involved in sales of property, estate inventories, and boundary disputes, the Godsoes left a body of measured plans, surveys,

and maps that today form part of the legal archives of town, regional, and state governmental bodies where they were recorded or where land disputes were adjudicated. In some rare instances, William Godsoe's plans have come to light among the personal papers or deeds records of early families. However, most are known as second- or third-generation copies by town clerks or court clerks of originals that have been lost.

One of the earliest plans by William Godsoe was prepared in 1697, not long after he was elected Kittery's Town Surveyor, in connection with the sale of 300 acres of land at Briant's Point, Kittery, by Elihu Gunnison to Gunnison's brother-in-law, John Ingerson. Godsoe's *Elihu Gunnison's Land at Brian's Point* (89), now lost, was copied twenty-five years later into the Kittery Town Records by the town clerk, Joseph Hammond, where it remains today. The elements that were to characterize much of Godsoe's witty and flamboyant mapping technique are evident in Hammond's copy: geese (or ducks or sea gulls) at the head of "Goose Creek"; a ship at anchor in the harbor; gabled seventeenth-century houses and outbuildings; a dramatic compass star. Another view of Briant's Point is provided by a Godsoe map made sixteen years later, in 1713, for Elihu Gunnison. While not so visually complex, Godsoe's *Mapp of his 300 acres of Land* (92) records four additional houses on Briant's Point and the continued subdivision of Gunnison's property among new owners.

A routine inventory of the estate of Francis Hooker of Kittery, ordered in 1715 by executors after the death of his widow, was the occasion for another Godsoe plan known only from its copy in the Kittery Town Records. *Late Major Hooke houselot lying neere Kittery Point* (93), recorded in 1716 by town clerk Joseph Ham-

mond, shows a small lot lying between Crockets Creek and the Piscataqua River. Besides an orchard, the plan illustrates a central-chimney seventeenth-century house with a "bull's-eye" medallion, apparently intended as a decorative device. Godsoe's 1701 *Plott of mʳ Humphrey Chadburns Farm att Sturgen Creek* (91), which was also an inventory-related survey, reveals similar architectural detail. Undertaken on behalf of Lucia Styleman, Chadburn's recently remarried widow, Godsoe's *Plott* measured Chadburn's property at Sturgeon Creek, which abutted the farm of Lt. Frost. The original plan is at the Maine State Archives and has a colorful, oversize compass star; more important is the lozenge-shaped hatchment over the doorway of the Frost home, hung there after the recent death of Lt. Frost's mother.

A Godsoe plan that survives not only as an original in the Maine State Archives but as second- and third-

generation clerks' copies was prepared following a dispute between the Kittery neighbors Christian Remick and Samuel Spinney after Remick accused the latter of felling sixty trees on his property. Dated 1697, *the Land in Controversey Claimed by mʳ Christan Remick and improved By Samull Spinney* (90) concluded that the trees in question grew on one of several parcels of land that made up the "old Lott" of Thomas Spinney. The document, illustrated by ducks and little houses, was copied into the Kittery Town Records by Joseph Hammond; a copy was also entered into the records of the Massachusetts Supreme Judicial Court, Suffolk County, Boston, by Elisha Cooke, court clerk.

The Godsoe mapping tradition was continued in Kittery by William's grandson, John Godsoe, who served as Town Surveyor after 1736. When he prepared the inventory survey, *Division of yᵉ Lands of mʳ John Hole Late*

91 DETAIL

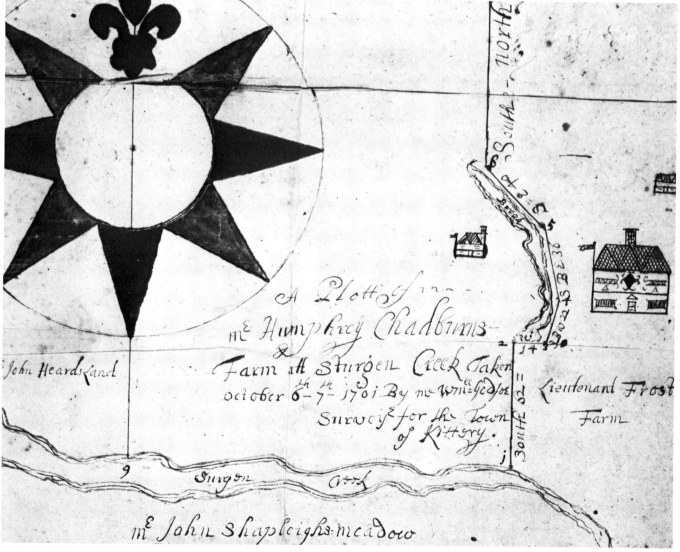

of Kittery Deceas.[d] (94), the younger Godsoe drew a more sophisticated tree symbol than that used by his grandfather to indicate orchards and undeveloped land. Like William, however, John Godsoe was careful with architectural detail, and his rendering of the 1734 middle parish meetinghouse by Curtice's Bridge at Spruce Creek provides a rare view of rural bell-tower architecture in the first half of the eighteenth century. The fortuitous survival of John Godsoe's original plan in the Whipple Family papers at the New Hampshire Historical Society, together with a manuscript copy of the plan (95) by Tobias Leighton, Kittery town clerk in 1740, reveals how accurately such maps were transcribed into the record books. Few departures in the style and detail of the drawings can be found in the copy and there are no important technical omissions or alterations.

William Godsoe was a homespun figure curiously out of step with the late Puritan period. He came to Salem, Massachusetts, as a mariner in the 1670s owning fifty-two books, a chestful of "divers mathmatical instruments," a "large sun dyall," a "bras circular dyall," and two pairs of brass compasses. He left Salem in 1684 following his conviction for complicity in the "Great Corwin Robbery" and for his escape from the Ipswich jail. The episode, in which he unsuccessfully quoted Scripture in his defense, involved his wife (she was the perpetrator of the robbery) and cost him both his instruments and his house. It also left him branded on the forehead with the letter *B* (for Burglar). Later, in his role as a surveyor, his depositions in Kittery court records reveal a man of Elizabethan wit, literacy, and forwardness. His professional acceptance in Kittery after 1685 was a reflection of a critical local need for surveyors.

References: Kittery; Suffolk County; Candee, "Land Surveys."

93 DETAIL

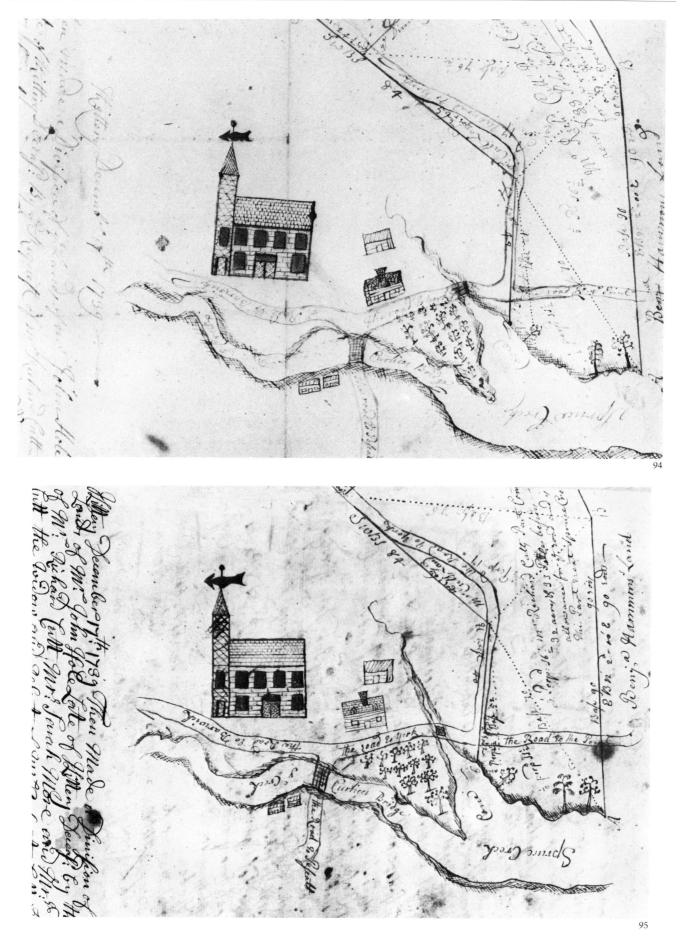

94

95

87

96

Canso, Fourt

George Follings

Nova Scotia, 1745

Manuscript, ink and watercolor; 22 × 20⅛ in.

Scale 1:250

New England Historic Genealogical Society

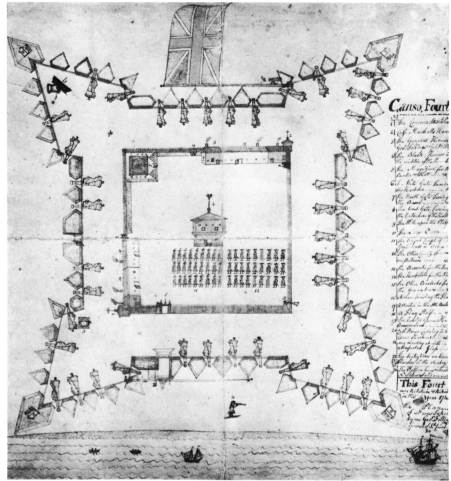

96

Fort Canso, an English fishing station and military outpost located at the straits of Canso off the eastern tip of Nova Scotia, was taken and burned by French troops in March 1745 shortly after the outbreak of King George's War. Within weeks, English troops had reoccupied the site for use as a staging point for an assault on the fortress of Louisburg on Cape Breton Island. According to instructions given by Massachusetts Governor William Shirley to William Pepperell, General Pepperell was to

> order two companies, consisting of forty men each with their proper officers on shore . . . and erect a block house frame, on the hill of Canso, where the old one stood, and hoist English colours upon it; enclosing it with pickets and pallisadoes, so that the sides of the square may extend about one hundred feet.

Shirley additionally ordered eight nine-pounder cannons to be installed "for the security of the harbor." Later that year the English and colonial forces won an impressive victory over the French at Louisburg, the first successful large-scale military undertaking attempted by American colonials in their recurring wars with the French in the seventeenth and eighteenth centuries.

The "Geoʳ Follingˢ Gunner" who drew and colored *Canso, Fourt* was George Follings, a First Lieutenant in Richard Gridley's Massachusetts Company and Regiment, who married Mary Smith in Boston in 1752 and who in 1745 shared a small house on the eastern flank of the fort with his co-gunner George Mills. Probably drawn to commemorate the role of the fort in the taking of Louisburg, Follings's plan follows the common convention of a cartographic plan on which are applied schematic and decorative drawings shown in elevation. The forty cannons lining the outer platform are considerably out of scale, as is the oversize flag. However, the number of cannons (increased from the stipulated eight), the two companies of grenadiers and musketeers, and the disposition of the pickets, palisades, barracks, sentry boxes, blockhouse, and shot and powder magazine no doubt accurately repre-

sent the layout and personnel of the fort as they then existed. Captain John Rouse, commander of a British vessel of war engaged in the Louisburg expedition, is shown entering the harbor. A round "large oven" stands against the inside east wall of the stockade; a round well operated by a rope and crank can be seen on the north face of the platform. Three manuscript plans of forts at Canso are on file at the Public Records Office, London.

References: Voye, 2031–32; Boston, *Marriages,* 3; PRO, 2:1130–32; Shirley.

97

Plot of the Interior of the Aquedneck Coal Mines near Newport Rhode Island

Unknown draftsman

Rhode Island, circa 1810
Manuscript, ink and watercolor; 19 × 11¾ in.
Scale 1:200
Newport Historical Society

Plot of the Interior of the Aquedneck Coal Mines near Newport Rhode Island depicts a mine in Portsmouth, Rhode Island, that had been the source of low-grade coal during much of the eighteenth century and that in 1810 was owned by the Aquedneck Company. Beginning at a point near the center of the tunnel complex, the plan notes the bearings and distances taken in three directions and schematically depicts the galleries left by earlier operations, as well as the known coal deposits that remained to be taken out. Notably lacking on this map is a compass indicator.

Early nineteenth-century mining operations consumed large quantities of capital, and the Aquedneck Company, like others who operated this mine, was constantly short of funds. Some monies were realized by means of a lottery approved by the Rhode Island General Legislature in October 1809. Still needing capital, however, the Aquedneck Company probably produced this manuscript map in order to attract private investors. A second, identical copy of this map is in the papers of the Aquedneck Company at the Newport Historical Society. Two principal veins of coal are shown on an 1849 map of Aquidneck Island; the map illustrated here is a mine of the eastern vein, which runs parallel to the "Turnpike Road."

References: Bolhouse; Hammett and Turner.

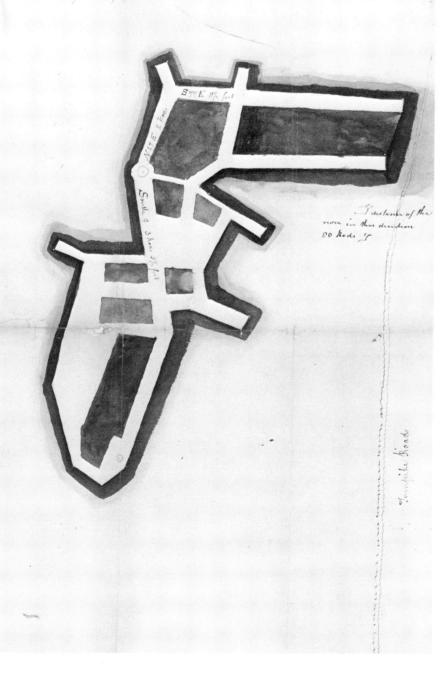

97

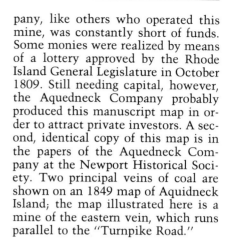

98*

Plan of Sandy Bay Pier

Jabez R. Gott (1794–1876)

Massachusetts, circa 1819 (Rockport)
Manuscript, ink and watercolor; 25 × 17 in.
Scale 1:400
Private Collection

The harbor at Sandy Bay, Gloucester, Massachusetts, was developed in two stages. The first was a short breakwater in 1811 on the northwest side of Bearskin Neck; the second was a longer breakwater in 1819 on the north side of the harbor directly facing the ocean. *Plan of Sandy Bay Pier*, by Jabez Richardson Gott, is a survey of harbor works prepared in 1819, when the longer or northern section of the breakwater was designed and built. The plan is illustrated with considerable detail and includes dwelling houses, outbuildings, fences, and a mechanical well pump (probably early for the time) — all shown in elevation. The configuration of the harbor, the large Federal house, and some of the piers are still extant. Jabez Gott lived to see this section of Gloucester become the town of Rockport. Calling himself a surveyor in his early years, he later acquired part ownership in the *Louisiana*, a commercial schooner not unlike the ones he drew on this plan. He served a term in 1842 as a school committeeman and died a "gentleman."

References: Babson, 544–46; Gloucester, 1:239; "Ship Registers," 177.

99

A Plat of The Village of Apponogue 1805

Sabin Lewis (fl. 1778–1819)

Rhode Island, 1805

Manuscript, ink and watercolor, and impressed details; 13⅞ × 22⅛ in. (fragment)

Scale 1:500

Rhode Island Historical Society

A Plat of The Village of Apponogue 1805 by Sabin Lewis is a subdivision map, probably commissioned by a joint stock company organized for the purpose of selling fifty or more waterfront lots in the center of Warwick, Rhode Island, when the town was just becoming industrialized in the beginning of the nineteenth century. Located at the head of Greenwich Bay, the new mill village was laid out on both sides of the Boston Post Road (shown as Broad Street on Sabin's map) and on the west and north shores of the bay.

Sabin Lewis was a professional mapmaker and a native of Rhode Island. Lewis received his cartographic training during the Revolution and published maps of the state in 1804 and 1807. *A Plat of The Village* is one of several identical fragments in the collection of the Rhode Island Historical Society. Labeled "Map No. 20," it suggests that Lewis had been commissioned to make as many maps as there were lots for sale in the development. If so, at least forty-nine other copies of this unusual and colorful map at one time were in circulation. To save time, he set type for and hand-printed the legend and descriptive components of the map, and carved what appear to be woodblocks illustrating standard two-floor and three-floor two-chimney dwelling or work houses seen in front elevation. He then printed the woodblocks ink-stamp fashion against a pen-and-watercolor outline of roads and waterways.

References: Chapin, *Check List*, 14, 20; Fuller, 150–59.

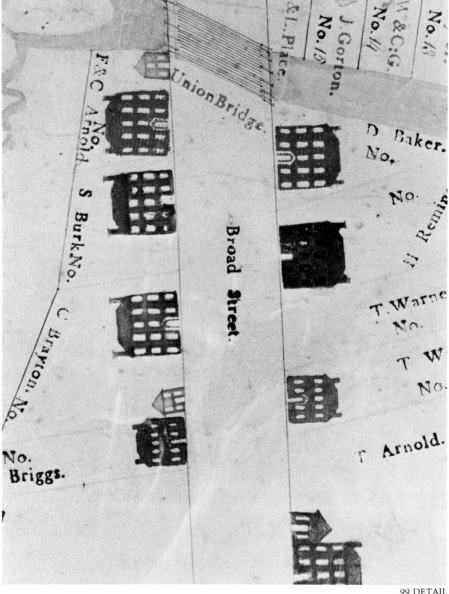

99 DETAIL

100 *

Map of the Town of Concord

Edmund Leavitt

New Hampshire, 1805

Manuscript, ink; 20¼ × 18 in. (sight)

Scale 1:40,000

New Hampshire State Library

101

A Plan of the Channel of the Merrimack River in 1804 & 1863

William Prescott (1788–1875)

New Hampshire, 1863

Manuscript, red ink and pencil; 16⅞ × 5¼ in.

Scale 1:40,000

New Hampshire Historical Society

The same low-lying intervales that made Concord, New Hampshire, desirable for planting in the early eighteenth century also made the town particularly vulnerable to erosion and to radical shifts and reversals in the channel of the Merrimack River. In an appendix to a paper read to the New Hampshire Historical Society in 1853, the natural scientist and genealogical historian William Prescott prepared a manuscript sketch in which he superimposed the riverbed of 1863 on a plan of the river as it was in 1804. Titled *A Plan of the Channel of the Merrimack River in 1804 & 1863*, the plan records shifts in the meander patterns of the Merrimack in Concord during the previous sixty years. Some alterations in the channel were artificial. The cut shown as 4 on Prescott's plan was trenched by the Northern Railroad Company in

1847; at that time the company was completing a link on the western bank of the river and did not wish to carry the expense of building and maintaining two unnecessary bridges. The elimination of Sugar-ball and Hale's points (15 and 16 on Prescott's plan), however, and the creation of a new meander called "The Fan" (13 and 14 on Prescott's Plan) were the results of winter freshets in 1828 and 1831. By combining his own memory with the recollection of earlier residents of the town, Prescott was able to measure changes in the relative length and width of the Sugar-ball and Hale's points before their final breaching by ice-choked floodwaters.

Edmund Leavitt's 1804 *Map of the Town of Concord*, on which Prescott's sketch was based, was commissioned at public auction to Leavitt at a cost of one hundred dollars. Although the details of the river appear to be accurate, Leavitt's survey did little more than fulfill the requirements of the 1803 New Hampshire mapping law and does not reflect the care and wealth of detail brought to many of the maps in the 1803 series. A licensed innkeeper in Concord during the years 1799 through 1803, Edward Leavitt served Concord as a selectman, constable, auditor, fence-viewer, surveyor of highways, and corder of wood. He was recorded as a grand-juryman for Rockingham County in 1812 and served his parish as tithingman in 1815.

Prescott's sketch is drawn to the same scale as Leavitt's map (200 rods to an inch); the "lead colour" contours of the river exactly match Leavitt's contours; and his compass pointer is a virtual copy of Leavitt's, in the same location.

References: Concord, 535–36; Prescott, *Memorial,* 318–23; Prescott "Report."

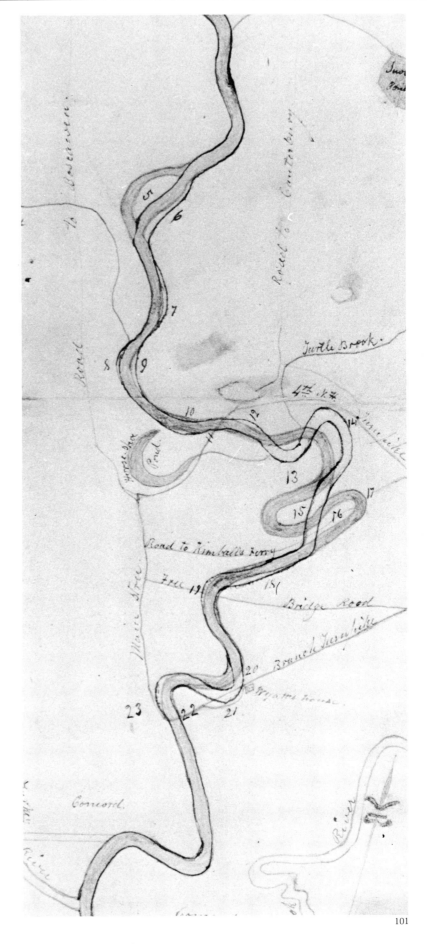

101

102

Plan of Suncook Village & Mills
Unknown draftsman
New Hampshire, circa 1830
Manuscript, ink; 12¼ × 30 in.
Scale 1:1,500
New Hampshire Historical Society

Just before it joins the Merrimack, the Suncook River in New Hampshire falls seventy-five feet over a distance of approximately six hundred yards. Located in what is now Pembroke, the falls have been the site of a succession of mechanical and industrial operations requiring water-power. The first of these was a grist mill and a sawmill erected in 1738 shortly after the settlement of nearby Penacook. A fulling mill was erected at this site in 1773, and carding, forge, tanning, and slitting mills by 1815. The first large-scale factory was built by the Lewis Company in 1817; cotton and planing mills followed in 1829 and 1843. In 1855 all water rights were consolidated under the Pembroke Mills Company.

The *Plan of Suncook Village & Mills* is a schematic layout of the dams, bridges, canals, roads, and mill buildings of the village complex as it looked shortly after the erection of the Lewis, Bates, and Williams mills in 1828. A bypass canal was cut in order to harness the middle falls most effectively. Major three-story work buildings, complete with bell towers, appear at the upper and lower dams. The close juxtapostion of mills, factory stores, and tenements in Suncook Village follows a formula that characterized scores of mill villages in New Hampshire (notably those at Harrisville, New Ipswich, Jaffrey, and Antrim) and that signaled the arrival of industrialization in America in the early nineteenth century; three of the four factory-owned "boarding houses" or "dwelling houses" appear to be one- or two-story wooden frame structures; the fourth is a three-story brick or wood structure. The existence of a second manuscript copy of the *Plan of Suncook Village & Mills*, as well as a *Plan of Suncook River* drawn by Benjamin Parker in 1829 (both of which specify in feet the fall of water between points of the river), suggests that this document was prepared during the negotiations of the sale of water rights and mill properties.

References: Carter and Fowler, 1: 354–55, 390.

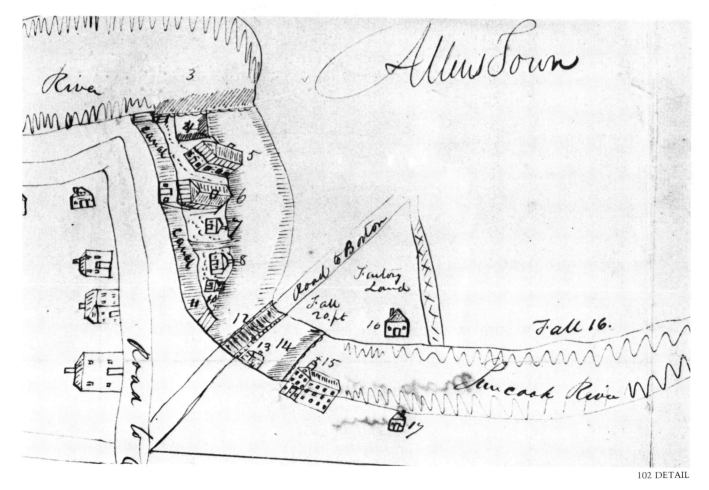

102 DETAIL

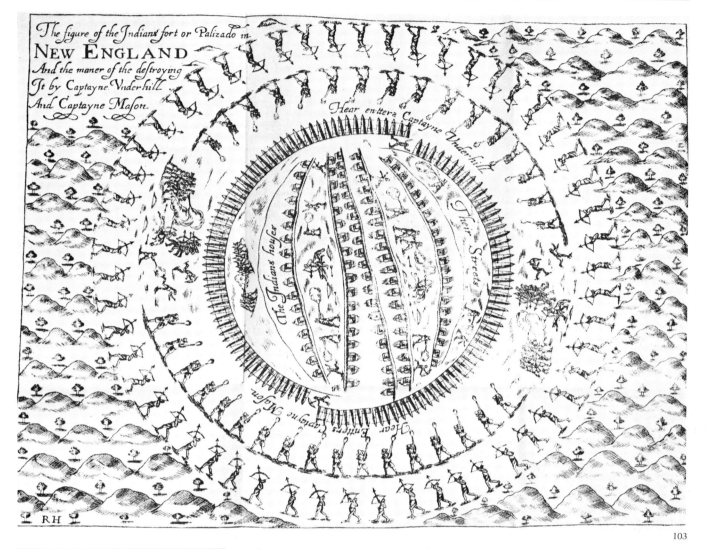

The figure of the Indians fort or Palizado in
NEW ENGLAND
And the maner of the destroying
It by Captayne Vnderhill
And Captayne Mason.

Hear enttera Captayne Vnderhill

The Indians houses

Their Streets

Hear Enttera Captayne Mason

RH

103

103

The figure of the Indians fort or Palizado in New England . . .

John Underhill (circa 1597–1672)
RH, artist or engraver

London, 1638
Photographic reproduction by J. Hyatt, London, 1891, No. 7; 11¾ × 20¾ in.
Scale 1:250

New England Historic Genealogical Society

Captain John Underhill, a military adventurer living in Boston, was sent to Connecticut by the Massachusetts government to assist John Mason in the English campaign against the Pequot tribe. *The figure of the Indians fort or Palizado in New England,* an engraved print signed with the initials RH, appeared in Underhill's history of the Pequot War published in London in 1638 and written during the winter of the previous year after Underhill had been disarmed, disenfranchised, and exiled from Massa-

chusetts as a supporter of the Antinomians. A plan illustrated with human figures, palisades, and wigwams shown in concentric elevation, the print depicts Mason and Underhill's attack on a principal Pequot village located just north of the present town of Stonington, Connecticut. The attack broke the morale of the Pequot nation, though some modern historians suggest that few, if any, Pequot warriors were present to defend the village. There is no way of knowing whether the engraving was based on a sketch submitted by Underhill himself, or whether it was the artist's interpretation of the text. Consistencies with the text include the Narragansett and eastern Niantic tribesmen who formed an outer ring around the enclosure, the number of wigwams (seventy), the number of English (seventy-seven), and the circular plan and two entrances of the palisade. Though appealing in its distinctively European design and cartographic technique, the map docu-

ments tragedy. If accurate, the plan is the earliest depiction of an Algonquian military structure in New England.

References: Jennings, 216–27; *DAB,* s.v. "John Underhill"; Palfrey, 1:184–93.

104

The Seat of War, in New England, by an American Volunteer, with The Marches of the Several Corps . . .

Unknown draftsman

London, 1775

Engraving with watercolor; printed for Robert Sayer and John Bennett; 29⅛ × 22⅜ in.

Scale 1:500,000

New Hampshire Historical Society

With the help of an unidentified American Tory serving with the English regulars in New England, the London firm of Robert Sayer and John Bennett offered for sale on 2 September 1775 a firsthand view of military engagements that had taken place in April, May, and June of that year. *The Seat of War, in New England, by an American Volunteer, with The Marches of the Several Corps* pinpoints and illustrates the site of each principal action. The "Bridge" and "19th April" identify the town of Concord, Massachusetts; Americans face the British on Bunker Hill; Charlestown is graphically depicted "in flames"; General Washington's forces — the Virginian Horse, the New York Grenadiers, and the forward "Piquets" — are shown on their march east to Boston.

Like Le Rouge's 1777 ectype *La Nouvelle Angleterre, The Seat of War, in New England* is a close copy of Braddock Mead's 1775 *Map of the most Inhabited part of New England* (12, 13). It superimposes by means of pictures military events taking place in 1775 on a 1750–1765 topography; the only new data are the network of roads traversed by the adversary armies and the location of troops, encampments, and battle engagements. The English public had no maps more recent than the Mead map or Mead-derived copies and therefore would not have perceived these inconsistencies. Sayer and Bennett continued to publish war maps, *The Theatre of War in America* appearing in 1776.

References: Stevens and Tree; Tooley, 50, 561; BL, *Printed*, 10:478.

104 DETAIL

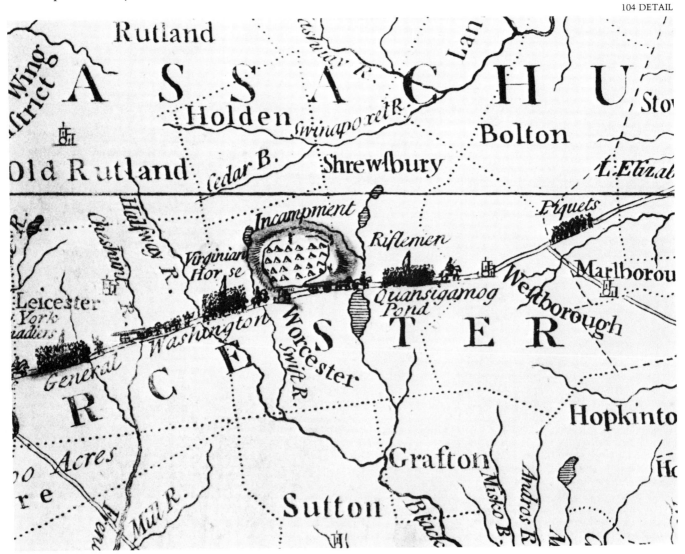

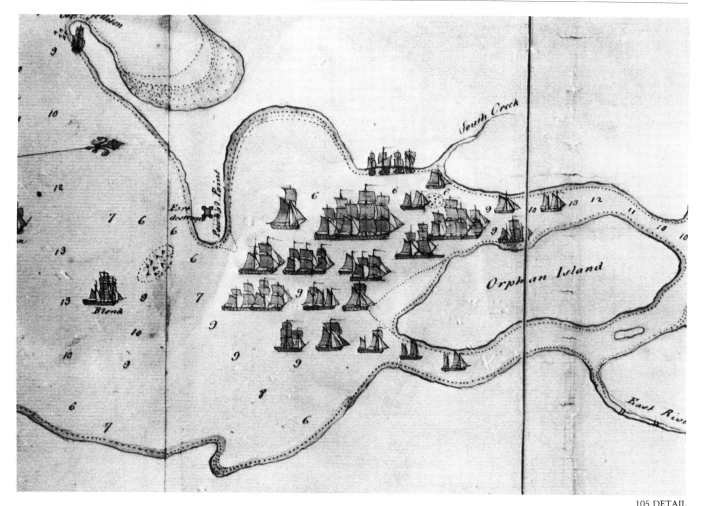

105

**Penobscot River and Bay with operations
of the English fleet**

Unknown draftsman

District of Maine, August 1779

Manuscript, ink and watercolor; 22 × 60
in.

Scale 1:14,000

Library of Congress

106 *

This Chart of Penobscot . . .

John Calef (1725–1812), artist (?)

Samuel Neele (1758–1824), engraver

London, 1781

Engraving; 23¾ × 17 in.

Published in Calef's *The Siege of Penobscot by the Rebels*

Scale 1:40,000 (inset 1:10,000)

John Carter Brown Library, Brown University

In 1779, four years after the battle of
Bunker Hill, English commanders in
New York sent a small fleet of sloops
and transports to secure the entrance
to Penobscot Bay in Maine and to prevent its use by American privateers.
Fort George was built by the English

on a peninsula in Majabigwaduce
Harbor, and three English men-of-war
with thirty-eight guns commanded by
Captain Henry Mowatt (127) were
stationed at the harbor's entrance. An
American force of nineteen ships
with 300 guns under Commodore
Dudley Saltonstall soon arrived to
dislodge the English but were successfully held off. The stalemate
ended about a month later when a
relief force of five additional English
warships pursued the American flo-
tilla up the Penobscot River and destroyed it.

The impressive English victory
over the American Penobscot expedition was celebrated by the publication in London of a journal kept by
an American loyalist, Dr. John Calef
(born in Ipswich, Massachusetts,
1726), who as a surgeon was an eyewitness to the siege and to the subsequent American defeat. Samuel
Neele, a London engraver, prepared a
map for Calef's journal under the title
Chart of Penobscot (106), illustrating
the destruction of the American fleet
on the Penobscot River; an inset
shows the three English men-of-war
holding the American fleet at bay.

*Penobscot River and Bay with oper-
ations of the English fleet* (105) depicts the English and American ships
in positions identical to those shown
on Neele's engraving, which may
have been based on this manuscript.

References: Kevitt; Tooley, 461, 97.

95

107

A Plan of the Town of Newport in Rhode Island

Charles Blaskowitz (fl. 1760–1825), cartographer

William Faden, engraver and publisher

London, 1 September 1777

Engraving; 14¾ × 21 in.

Scale 1:6,000

Newport Historical Society

Newport, Rhode Island, located on the southern tip of Aquidneck Island, was occupied by British soldiers from December 1776 to October 1779. During this period, half the population of the town left Aquidneck Island for points on the mainland; British troops roamed the island at will for food and firewood; loyalists entertained the English officers under command of General Richard Prescott. In 1778, American troops under General John Sullivan of Massachusetts, who were attempting to dislodge the British, occupied the entire island except for the last fortifications around Newport itself. The effort failed, and Sullivan's troops withdrew. *A Plan of the Town of Newport in Rhode Island* by Charles Blaskowitz was issued by the engraver and publisher William Faden after the first year of British occupation of the town. A gifted artist, Blaskowitz had been assigned in 1753 to the British Corps of Engineers at the Tower of London as a twelve-year-old cadet draftsman. He joined Samuel Holland's survey team in North America in 1764 and later gained a reputation as one of the ablest military surveyors for the British armies during the Revolution. So well regarded were his talents that two years before the English occupation of Newport, the *Massachusetts Gazette* for 5 May 1774 informed its readers that "an exact survey of our Seacoast . . . from Plymouth round the Cape to Rhode Island government is intended by Mr. Blaskowitz." His map of Newport, together with others he made of the Narragansett area, was drawn in the course of this 1774 survey. Manuscript copies of these surveys were probably carried by the English troops who took Aquidneck Island in 1776.

107

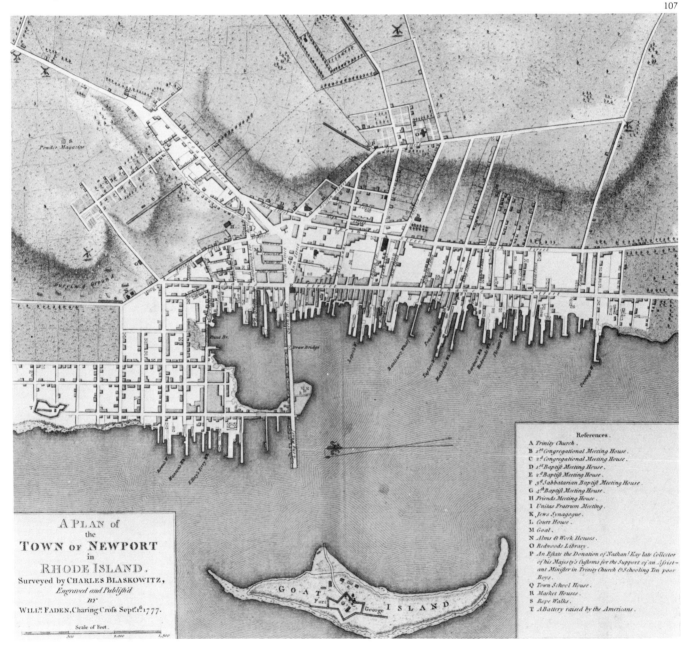

A PLAN of the TOWN OF NEWPORT in RHODE ISLAND.

Surveyed by CHARLES BLASKOWITZ,

Engraved and Publish'd

BY

WILL. FADEN, Charing Cross Sept. 1.ᵗ 1777.

Scale of Feet.

References.

A Trinity Church.
B 1ˢᵗ Congregational Meeting House.
C 2ᵈ Congregational Meeting House.
D 1ˢᵗ Baptist Meeting House.
E 2ᵈ Baptist Meeting House.
F 3ᵈ Sabbatarian Baptist Meeting House.
G 4ᵗʰ Baptist Meeting House.
H Friends Meeting House.
I Unitas Fratrum Meeting.
K Jews Synagogue.
L Court House.
M Goal.
N Alms & Work Houses.
O Redwoods Library.
P An Estate the Donation of Nathan.ˡ Kay late Collector of his Majesty's Customs for the Support of an Assistant Minister in Trinity Church & Schooling Ten poor Boys.
Q Town School House.
R Market Houses.
S Rope Walks.
T A Battery raised by the Americans.

A manuscript version of Blaskowitz's Newport map (a copy of which was undoubtedly used by Faden for the engraving) is in the collection of the Clements Library.

References: Marshall and Peckham, 30; Winsor, *Narrative,* 6:597; Cumming, 26; Klemp, *Maps,* 39.

108

[A Section of Boston Overrun by Fire]

Jeremy Belknap (1744–1798)

Boston, 23 April 1787

Manuscript, ink and pencil; 9¼ × 7¼ in. Scale 1:2,600

Massachusetts Historical Society

Between the years 1702 and 1794 portions of Boston were devastated by fire on fifteen occasions. The day following the Boston fire of 22 April 1787, Jeremy Belknap, who had just resigned his ministry in Dover, New Hampshire, and was visiting the port town, composed a letter to his friend Ebenezer Hazard which today is included among the Belknap papers at the Massachusetts Historical Society. Belknap was an eyewitness to the fire and had assisted his colleague Mather Byles of the Hollis Street Church in recovering Byles's papers and property. Enclosed with his letter was "a small plan or sketch," in ink, on which the progress of the fire was marked in pencil. Belknap noted in the letter that the fire began in a dockside malt house on the heels of a two-day dry northeasterly wind. Burning chips of wood spread the fire to structures on the far side of the dock, and the blaze eventually consumed seventy-eight buildings with a property loss of £20,000. Belknap's sketch accurately depicts the street layout and principal buildings of what is now downtown Washington Street. A dotted line denotes the direction taken by the burning embers blown from the malt house and the extent of the fire as it spread downwind in a southwesterly direction. The 1737 Hollis Street meetinghouse, shown in the sketch as a side elevation, was one of the losses. (It was rebuilt from designs prepared by Charles Bulfinch using an innovative domed interior and twin bell towers.) Jeremy Belknap, later noted for his superb three-volume *History of New Hampshire,* was one of the founders of the Massachusetts Historical Society.

References: Whitehill, 50; Belknap, Jeremy, "Sketch plan."

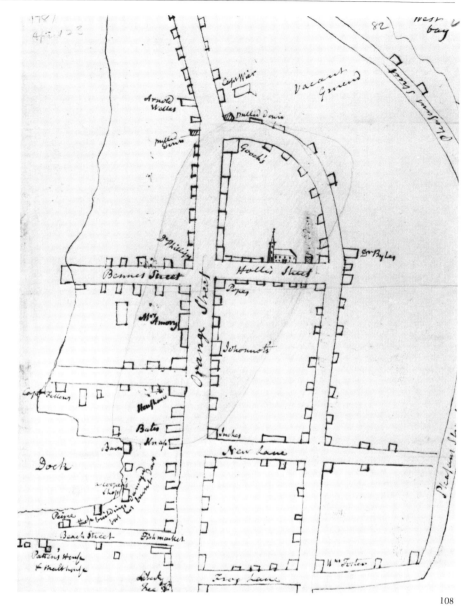

108

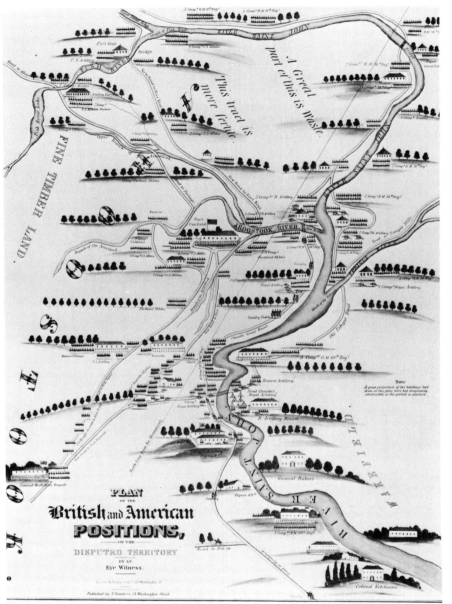

109

Plan of the British and American Positions, on the Disputed Territory by an Eye Witness

Unknown draftsman

Boston, 1843
Colored lithograph by Bouve and Sharp; published by Nathaniel Dearborn, Boston; 29½ × 22½ in. (sight)
Scale 1:200,000
Maine State Museum

The so-called "Aroostook War" consisted of a confrontation between English troops and American militiamen over the location of the boundary between the State of Maine and the Province of New Brunswick in 1839. Precipitated by reciprocal arrests by English and American authorities in the area of Madawaska on the St. John River, the confrontation drew some 1,300 fusileers and regulars of the British army and fifty thousand Maine militiamen and American troops either in the Aroostook region or on their way there. General Winfield Scott was ordered to the scene by President Van Buren, and the affair was peaceably negotiated. *Plan of the British and American Positions, on the Disputed Territory by an Eye Witness*, published as a lithograph four years after the event (and a year after the Webster-Ashburton Treaty permanently fixed the Maine–New Brunswick boundary), schematically locates the dispositions of the opposing troops at the climax of the affair. The purpose of the map is commemorative rather than cartographic. The relative sizes and configurations of the St. John, Aroostook, and Tubique rivers appear to have been determined by the number of troops and barracks that the cartographer needed to fit into the spaces between them and by the length of the various place names.

References: Hatch, 272–76.

110*
Powder Horn

Made the 6th. of September AD 1775 at Roxbury Camp for Captain Thomas Kempton

Unknown engraver

Roxbury, Mass., 1775

Horn and wood; L. 12 in., DIAM. 4⅝ in. (base)

John S. du Mont

111*
Powder Horn

John Chase, his horn made in the year 1776, in April ye 9th by Samuel French

Horn and wood; L. 12½ in., DIAM. 4½ in. (base)

Scale 1:90,000

John S. du Mont

112*
Powder Horn

CAPT JEREMIAH EAMES/JANUARY YE 7th 1776

Captain Jeremiah Eames (1735–1817) or his son Jeremiah Eames (b. 1762)

Northumberland, N.H., 1776

Horn and pine; L. 13⅜ in., DIAM. 3 in. (base)

New Hampshire Historical Society

113*
Powder Horn

PROVIDENCE F 1777 STEPHEN AVERY his horn

Stephen Avery (?)

Rhode Island, 1777

Horn and wood; L. 14½ in., DIAM. 5⅛ in. (base)

Scale 1:6,000

Rhode Island Historical Society

Powder containers made from cows' horns were in use by American militiamen and soldiers during the last French and Indian War (1756–1763) and the first two years of the Revolutionary War (1775–1776). For purposes of identification, their owners often inscribed and decorated them on the shaved inner layer of the horn. Inscriptions and decorations were sometimes the work of professional engravers who traveled with the American regiments and whose work can be recognized by type and by style. Map horns — powder horns decorated with a map or view — are rare. They were produced mostly during inactive periods of military readiness such as the American siege of Boston from April 1775 through March 1776 and frequently depict the siege-works and forts where the inactive troops spent their time. The four military map horns included in the exhibition were selected from forty-four examples of known map horns with New England subjects.

Made the 6th. of September AD 1775 at Roxbury Camp for Captain Thomas Kempton was inscribed in the beginning of the sixth month of the Boston siege by an unknown, probably professional engraver at the request (or on the behalf) of Captain Kempton, who was stationed on the American side of the siege-works at Roxbury Neck. The lighthouse, windmill, church spires, and foreshortened views of gabled dwelling houses might have been seen from the American side, either by the naked eye or through a spyglass. By contrast, *John Chase, his horn made in the year 1776, in April ye 9th by Samuel French*, which was inscribed after the evacuation of Boston by the English, bears a relatively accurate map of Boston Harbor, giving the location of the principal forts and populated towns. Houses in "BOSTⁿ" and "Charlstown" are shown in rather cramped, three-quarter perspective; but those in "R:Bery" (Roxbury) are shown in the traditional side elevation laid down away from the central street. Besides serving at the siege of Boston, John Chase had marched to the Concord-Lexington skirmish. Appropriately, the figures of two "amerricans" are shown firing their muskets at three fleeing "Reglars."

CAPT JEREMIAH EAMES/ JANUARY YE 7th 1776, carved on a remote frontier outpost in northern New England, illustrates a wide area that includes Coos County, New Hampshire, and a portion of the Connecticut River. It cites the names and grant dates of towns along the "Portland Road" leading to the Maine coastline. At the base of the horn is shown "the Garrison House" at Northumberland, New Hampshire, where Captain Eames was stationed.

PROVIDENCE F 1777 STEPHEN AVERY his horn is decorated with a skillfully executed map of Providence. Among the recognizable buildings are the College, the 1775 Baptist meetinghouse, the Town House, the Beneficent Congregational Church, and the First Congregational Church. The Avery horn and possible February date closely correspond to a February 19, 1777 horn inscribed on behalf of Charles Hewitt of Philadelphia, who is known to have enlisted at Boston in Colonel Crane's artillery a month before his horn was engraved. This suggests that both map horns were copied from the same source or that both were engraved by the same hand on approximately the same date. It is also possible that neither Charles Hewitt nor Stephen Avery was billeted in Providence, but selected a Providence map from a number of decorative motifs offered by a professional horn engraver circulating among regiments in Boston or elsewhere.

Regardless of its source, the quality and detail of the 1777 Avery map horn make it comparable to the 1790 Fitch memory map of Providence (67). The town had grown considerably in the thirteen intervening years, particularly in the area of Rhode Island College (Brown University). It had also lost the double row of earthworks that were erected by the townspeople to discourage English attacks on the town.

References: Granscay, 294, Plates XXIII, XXIX; du Mont, 78, 84; "JESSE:STARr"; "Powder Horn Maps"; "Powder Horn"; "PROVIDENCE."

114*
Priming Flask

W. Beede Sandwich 1800

William Beede (b. 1781)

New Hampshire, 1800

Horn and wood; L. 8 in., DIAM. 3¼ in. (base)

Scale 1:80,000

Paul Bernheimer's Antique Arts

The widespread use of cartridges after 1777 made most powder horns obsolete: it was more convenient, and considerably more effective, for a soldier to carry containers of paper-wrapped powder and ball than to try to load a musket in the conventional, slower way. Priming flasks, however, which provided the small amount of powder necessary to ignite a flintlock firing mechanism, continued to be carried well into the nineteenth century. These were much smaller than powder horns and usually were made of hollowed wood or leather. *W. Beede Sandwich 1800*, a priming flask made from a cow's horn, is the only known example of a map horn carved with an accurate plan of a rural New England town. Its presumed maker was William Beede, the son of Nathan Beede (and grandson of Judge Daniel Beede), one of the early Quaker settlers of Sandwich, New Hampshire, and a member of the largest family in that town. William was disowned in 1810.

References: Merrill, Georgia D., 667–69; "Sandwich."

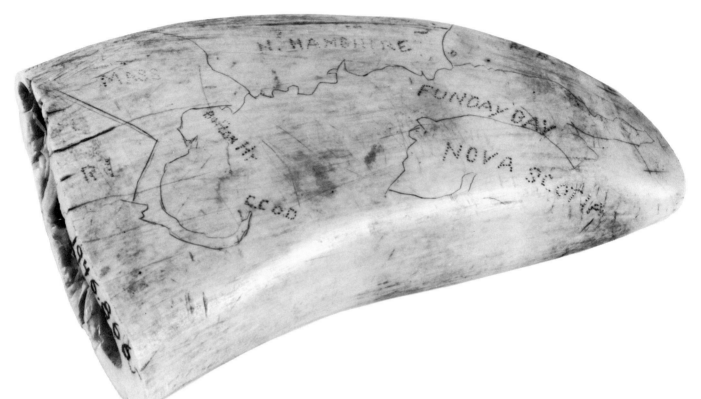

115

115
Scrimshaw Map

C Cod Boston H Nova Scotia . . .

Unknown engraver

New England (?), before 1820

Whale's tooth; L. 6 in., DIAM. 4⅛ in. (base)

Scale 1:2,000,000

Yarmouth Historical Society

Few whale teeth were engraved with charts or maps. This example from the Historical Society at Old Yarmouth was collected by the brothers George and William Bray, who were active in Yarmouth, Massachusetts, from 1860 to 1940 and who gave to the Society a collection of Mashpee Indian arrowheads and whale's tooth scrimshaw. This tooth bears a crude sketch map of the eastern coastline of New England from Cape Cod to the Bay of Fundy and Nova Scotia. Principal features are identified with a stippled inscription, including "Boston Hr" and "N.B." (New Brunswick). Eighteenth-century scrimshaw is rare, and the tooth presumably dates from the early nineteenth century, probably before 1820 because Maine is not shown. A whale tooth inscribed with a sketch chart of Boston Harbor in 1790 is part of the collection of the Marine Historical Association.

References: Carpenter.

116*

Surveyor's Chain

Maker unknown

New England, eighteenth or early nineteenth century

Iron; L. 33 ft.

Lempster Historical Society

Each component of this fifty-link surveyor's chain is 1.192 inches long, making a total length of 33 feet or 2 rods. It represents one half of a one-hundred-link Gunter chain, named after the English astronomer Edmund Gunter (1581–1626). Developed in the early seventeenth century, Gunter chains differed from Rathborne's decimal chain in that they were based on a "statute" rod of 16½ feet. Both were used by English surveyors and chainmen for measuring distance, but only the Gunter type was used in America. Fifty-link chains may have been preferred in America because long chains tended to get caught in the dense woods and underbrush. By contrast, English surveyors, who were measuring land many centuries under cultivation, continued to use one-hundred-link versions.

The original owner of this chain has not been identified but presumably was a New Hampshire surveyor. A fifty-link chain owned by the Stratham, New Hampshire, tanner and surveyor Samuel Lane (active circa 1748–1754) has connecting links and end handles similar to it. This style of fabrication was probably continued into the early nineteenth century.

References: Lane, *Journal*, 32–33; Richeson, 108–9.

117

Surveyor's Compass

Joseph Halsy (fl. 1697–1762)

Boston, circa 1725–1750

Unidentified wood, hand-colored engraved
compass card, steel, glass; L. 11 in.,
DIAM. 5⅞ in., H. of bars 2½ in., L. of
needle 4⅝ in.

New Hampshire Historical Society

118

Surveyor's Compass and Sight

Unknown maker

Massachusetts (?), eighteenth century

Unidentified wood (probably pine), glass,
metal needle, paper compass card, traces
of red paint; H. 58½ in. (overall), DIAM.
5½ in. (compass face), L. 14½ in.,
W. 7½ in. (compass)

Historical Society of Old Newbury

The ban on metallurgy and the high
cost of imported brass encouraged the
making of wooden surveying instruments in the American colonies.
Among the most common of these
instruments were compasses that,
like the two eighteenth-century examples illustrated here, were con-
structed from hollowed-out wood and
provided with a glass cover secured
with putty. The first example, signed
by Joseph Halsy of Boston, has an engraved compass card with the cus-
tomary fleur-de-lys for the northern
point and with each principal quadrant marked off into ninety divisions.
Seven personified "Arts," including
"Logick," "Geometry," and "Mu-
sicke," decorate the seven remaining
directional pointers. The decorative
use of a ship at sea (rather than an
English crown, a Tudor rose, or the
figure of Britannia) suggests the engraving, and probably the compass itself, dates after the middle of the
eighteenth century. Halsy is the earliest known maker of wooden instruments in Boston and advertised a
newly invented quadrant in the *Boston Gazette* in 1738 under the name
"Joseph Halsey Jun." He was the old-
est of three brothers engaged in the
making of scientific and mathemati-
cal instruments. One brother, John
Halsy, abandoned the trade to become
a pirate. A second brother, James, was
one of the founders of the New Brick
Church in Boston and a Fourth Ser-
geant in the Artillery Company.

The second compass is by an unknown maker. It has wooden sights
and a stand that consists of a turned
base and three curved, thin legs.
(Some compasses were supported on
a single iron-pointed wooden staff dri-
ven into the ground, known as a Ja-

117

118

cob's staff.) The paper card of this compass is hand-lettered. A checklist compiled by the Smithsonian Institution in 1964 revealed that all the known makers of surviving wooden compasses lived and worked in New England towns. Only two makers outside of New England advertised such instruments.

References: Smart, 68; Bedini, 80–83.

References: Parker, 14–27, 251; Patten, 381; Richeson, 126–29; Black, "Mapping," 119.

119 *
George King his Book
George King
New Hampshire, eighteenth century
Bound manuscript notebook, ink; 14 × 9 in.
Bedford Historical Society

120 *
Geodaesia: or, The Art of Surveying and Measuring the Land Made Easie
John Love (fl. 1688–1711)
London, 1760
Bound volume, seventh edition of a publication first issued in 1688; 7⅞ × 5 in. (closed)
New Hampshire Historical Society

Unlike compasses and other navigation and surveying tools that were made locally in the American colonies, printed surveying manuals and textbooks continued to originate in England. First issued in 1688, *Geodaesia: or, The Art of Surveying and Measuring the Land Made Easie* was written by John Love, who practiced as a surveyor in North Carolina and in Jamaica before returning to England to write his text. *Geodaesia* was the first manual to address the special problem of surveying in America, and it went through at least seven English editions before 1760, and three English and two American editions between 1760 and 1796. The original owner of this copy was Peter Green, presumably a New Hampshire surveyor of the late eighteenth century.

As a supplement to such texts, apprentice or student surveyors compiled manuscript manuals. *George King his Book* is a seventy-page collection of problems and calculations arranged in increasing difficulty. A proprietor of Wolfeborough, New Hampshire, Captain George King may have been a student or colleague of the surveyor Matthew Patten of Bedford, New Hampshire, who cites a George King in his diary in 1778. Most of the calculations in King's book were hypothetical examples, but in some instances he recorded actual surveys including one of his own land (share number 13, consisting of 400 acres) abutting Smiths pond and Kings Cove in Wolfeborough. George King's use of seventeenth-century post windmills as pictographs and of English topographic terms such as "Crabtree Close" and "Turfey Lease" suggests that his source was one of the twenty-three English surveying manuals published in the seventeenth and eighteenth centuries.

121*

A North East View of the Great Town of Boston

William Burgis (fl. 1716–1731), artist

Boston, 1723
Monochrome reproduction by Meriden Gravure, 1975; 9¾ × 12¾ in.
Facsimile of an engraving attributed to Burgis

Essex Institute

122

A South East View of yᵉ Great Town of Boston in New England in America

William Burgis (fl. 1716–1731), artist
John Harris (fl. 1686–1740), engraver
William Price (1684–1771), publisher

Boston, 1743
Engraving in three sections; altered state of 1725 plates; 23¼ × 51¼ in.

American Antiquarian Society

123

a vew of Boston

John Smibert (1688–1751)

Boston, 1738
Oil on canvas; 30 × 50 in.

Childs Gallery

Shortly after John Bonner issued his 1722 map of Boston (52), subscriptions for the first printed view of the town were advertised in the *New-England Courant* by William Burgis, who promised that a drawing of the town from the northeast would soon be sent to England for engraving. Similar announcements promising northeast views were made by William Price and Thomas Selby in 1723. While no evidence has survived that these advertised views were actually

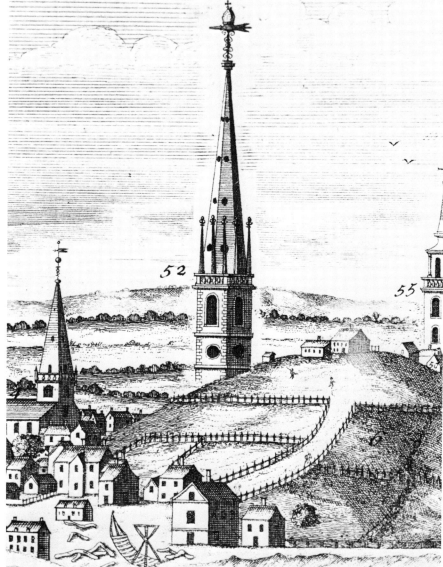

122 DETAIL

122

122 DETAIL

printed, the unsigned *North East View of the Great Town of Boston* (121), known from a single copy at Salem's Essex Institute, probably dates from this decade and is attributed to Burgis on the basis of a later advertisement by Price for subscriptions for a southeast view — implying that Price had given up on his northeast view. Whoever the artist (its engraver has not been identified), the *North East View* is the first printed document to give substance and dimension to the 1728 Burgis and the 1722–1769 Bonner-Price maps of Boston.

Taken from a promontory on Noddles Island, the northeast projection reveals a sequence of church and meetinghouse spires and bell towers that conforms to the 1728 Burgis

map: Christ, New North, New Brick, Brattle, King's Chapel, Old Brick, Old South, New South. The north flank of Long Wharf is seen at an approximate angle of thirty degrees. The extension of this wharf into Boston Harbor is out of perspective with the view of the town itself and greatly exaggerates its length. An unsolved question is why Christ Church, accurately depicted in the view with its rear apse, has a multi-storied belltower spire that was not voted for by the churchwardens until 1737 and not actually built until 1740. Either the date of the view must be questioned or the spire seen as the wishful thinking of Burgis, a churchman, whose colleague William Price later provided its design.

The large three-panel *South East*

View of ye Great Town of Boston in New England in America (122), signed by William Burgis and engraved by John Harris of London in 1725, is taken from Castle Island. (The legends "Fort George on Bird Island" and "Noddles Island Flatts" are later, added inaccuracies.) Two states of the plates are known (1725 and 1743), both issued by William Price; these are supplemented by a set of printed "pasters" designed to bring the 1725 spires up to 1736. The southward shift in the projection creates a subtle shift in the sequence of spires: New North is to the right of Christ; Old Brick, to the right of King's Chapel. The south flank of Long Wharf is seen at an approximate thirty-degree angle, though again the bird's-eye perspective of the wharf, as opposed to the promontory perspective of the town, puts the apparent length of the wharf greatly out of scale. A similar exaggeration inflates the height and size of the meetinghouse spires and the principal buildings of the town, some of which are shown up to ten times their actual size.

Artistically and technically, *A South East View of the Great Town* is a compelling and brilliant work that offers a wealth of architectural and topographic detail concerning Boston — more than any other single document of the eighteenth century. It has some fictional elements. The Brookline meetinghouse, for example, did not receive the tower shown in the 1743 state until 1770. The Trinity tower, surmounted by a gi-

gantic bishop's hat in the 1743 state, may be pure invention. Its accuracies, however, far outweigh the artistic license taken by Burgis and the engraver or engravers who altered the plate under the direction of William Price.

An important painted view of Boston closely related to the printed Price-Burgis view of 1736 was discovered and identified in 1976 by the Childs Gallery, Boston. Regarded now as the "vew of Boston" that was cited by John Smibert in his notebook in 1738, this landscape is the earliest painted representation of the town and reinforces, with color, the detailed architectural and topographic data of Burgis's three-panel southeast view. John Smibert was known for his fondness of "Landskips" in the Ital-

ianate style and used elements of Boston's topography as partial backgrounds for his portraits. The likeness of Francis Brinley, painted shortly after his arrival in Boston in 1729, has in its background a view of Beacon Hill and the Old South Meeting House. Smibert's *vew of Boston* (123), however, is the only known complete view of the town, and the only painting attributed to him that was conceived as a landscape study.

Like Burgis's 1723 *North East View of the Great Town*, John Smibert's *vew of Boston* was taken from Noddles Island in Boston Harbor, probably from Camp Hill, which was used for pasturing sheep. Its twelve ecclesiastical spires conform to the twelve shown on the 1736 "pasters" version of the Price-Burgis *South East View*.

123 DETAIL

This raises the question of sources. As a member of Boston's closely knit community of artists, Smibert was no doubt familiar with the William Burgis views of 1723 and 1725 and indeed with other published views that may have not survived. He may have used these views in filling out specific details of his landscape. Important differences between Burgis's and Smibert's handling of perspective and scale, however, argue that this study was essentially Smibert's own. Long Wharf is a case in point: while present to a limited degree, the exaggerated caricature length of the wharf in the 1725 southeast view (which Smibert's study most closely resembles) is absent in the painted landscape. Equally important, the exaggerated sizes and heights of the meetinghouses that characterize both the northeast and the southeast Burgis views, are softened and more realistic in the painting.

The discovery of this painting has reopened the question of Trinity's tower. Both the spireless "pasters" version and the full-blown "bishop's hat" versions of this tower that are depicted in the 1736 and 1743 Price-Burgis views have been regarded as William Price's inventions. The reappearance of the "pasters" version on the 1738 Smibert view, together with a request in the Trinity records of 1751 for funds to "repair the turret," suggests that some form of tower, indeed, was built.

References: Smibert, 95; Childs; Reps; Holman, "Burgis."

124

124

Newport, R.I. in 1730

Unknown artist

Rhode Island, circa 1740–1760

Lithograph by John P. Newell (circa 1830–1898), printed by J. H. Bufford, Boston, 1864; 20½ × 30 in.

Based on an overmantel painting in a house in Newport

Newport Historical Society

125

[Painted Fireboard with a View of Beverly Mass.]

Unknown artist

Salem, Mass., circa 1820

From the Andrew Safford house, Salem, built in 1818

Oil on wood; 31½ × 49 in.

Essex Institute

Painted representations of eighteenth- and early nineteenth-century New England towns were not limited to Boston. John P. Newell's *Newport, R.I. in 1730*, a lithograph print published by J. H. Bufford of Boston in 1864, was copied from a painted overmantel view from the Cottrell-Mumford-Watts-Phillips house on Mill Street, Newport, titled *Newport, R.I. 1740*. Newell's print, which is incorrectly dated, is a view of Newport as it appeared in the middle of the

eighteenth century. With minor exceptions — such as the perspective of the fort in the foreground, and the starboard rather than leeward orientation of the booms of a schooner under sail — it is an accurate rendering of the painted original. Taken from Goat Island in Newport Harbor, the view encompasses most of the area depicted in the 1777 Blaskowitz plan of Newport (107). The principal ecclesiastic spires and towers include the 1699 Friends meetinghouse, the meetinghouse of the First Congregational Society on Clarke Street, Trinity Church, and the meetinghouse of the Second Congregational Society on Mill Street. The Colony House stands near the center. The well-known round stone tower, believed to be the base of an early wind-operated grist mill, is visible just to the right of Mill Street; six wooden windmills stand on the bluffs overlooking the town. The appearance of Trinity's tower casts at least some doubt on the date of this view. First built in 1726, Trinity's tower fell down in a storm in 1731 and was not rebuilt until 1760. Since the extent of urban development shown in both the overmantel painting and Newell's copy is generally compatible with the 1764–1777 Blaskowitz plan of Newport, the 1740 date indicated in the painting may be twenty years too early.

Townscapes were also painted on partitions that closed off fireplaces when not in use. As on overmantels, realistic landscapes and townscapes on fireboards were much more rare than imaginary ones or stylized imitations of printed sources. A circa 1818 fireboard from the Andrew Safford house, Salem, now in the collection of the Essex Institute, has a superbly executed oil painting of an eastern view of the town of Beverly and a portion of north Salem, unquestionably one of the finest examples of its type to survive in New England. Possibly the work of a Scottish-born artist, Robert Cowan, who painted fireboards in Salem in the late eighteenth century, the view is taken from Ledge Hill in North Salem. Two ecclesiastic spires belonging to the first and north parishes are visible, both yellow in color. The 1,484-foot wooden Essex Bridge, built in 1788, crosses Beverly Harbor to Raymond's tavern in Beverly.

References: Rose, 412–13; Sinnott, 186–87; Downing, 140–41; Little, Nina F., *Wall Painting*, 61, 67; Little, Nina F., *Country Arts*, 189; Lovett; Bentley, 1:104–5; Smith, E. Vale, 61; Waterbury.

125 illustrated p. ii.

1763

The Packes James Gilmore of Portsmouth Oned by mr Jonath Warner a Sick Pasenger from the Island of Granards and Sant martens To Marblehead

126

126

**a South East Vew of the Town of Marble-
head**

Ashley Bowen (1728–1813)

Massachusetts, 1763

Ink and watercolor drawing in Bowen's
manuscript diary; 2½ × 6 in. (image),
7½ × 6 in. (sheet)

Marblehead Historical Society

Another source of townscapes and
coastal views is sketches of New England by amateur artists and diarists.
Unlike the stylized compositions of
William Burgis and his later imita-
tors, these tended to be realistic, eye-
level views in the tradition of coastal
profiles used by pilots and mariners
in navigating the shoreline. Among
the earliest of this genre are the drawings of Governor John Winthrop who
left in his journal simplified profiles
of points on the coast of Maine as
they appeared in the second and third
decades of the seventeenth century.
A later and more ambitious example
is the watercolor sketches of Ashley
Bowen, a seaman and sail maker
whose home was Marblehead, Massachusetts, and who kept a log in the
years from 1741 to 1813 recording the
names of ships and officers, their des-
tinations, and notable incidents at
sea. *A South East Vew of the Town
of Marblehead* was drawn by Bowen
after his voyage from Granada and St.
Martin aboard the brig *Success* under
Captain James Gilmore. (Bowen "put
on Shore Sick" in Marblehead while
the brig continued the following day
to Portsmouth, New Hampshire.) The
town is seen as it appeared to Bowen
"this 6 day of November 1763 the last
Time of my going to Sea for 20 years."
The three ecclesiastic spires are those
of St. Michael's Church (left), the new
meetinghouse (middle), and the old
meetinghouse (right). Bowen's drawings are the only known views of St.
Michael's tower.

References: Bowen, Ashley, 1:v–x, 2:Plate
XXVI; Winthrop, 2:260.

127

The Town of Falmouth, Burnt, by Captain Moet, Octb! 18th 1775

John Norman (circa 1748–1817), engraver

Boston, 1782

Engraving, 7¼ × 11¾ in.

Published as the frontispiece to *An Impartial History of the War in America,* volume 2

New Hampshire Historical Society

One of the most bitter episodes in the Revolutionary War — the burning of Falmouth, Maine — was the subject of a bird's-eye view engraved by John Norman in 1782 for the frontispiece of the second volume of *An Impartial History of the War in America.* The episode was the culmination of a chain of events that began in May 1775 when a Falmouth merchant whose business had been hurt by patriot nonimportation policies, procured the help of the Englishman Captain Henry Mowatt in order to unload some recently arrived English-made goods. The patriots countered by arresting Mowatt, seizing his longboats, and ransacking the merchant's household. In October 1775, Captain Mowatt executed "a just punishment of the town of Falmouth" by giving its residents two hours to vacate and then burning the town by means of point-blank fire from four naval vessels lying in the harbor. British seamen landed and set additional fires. Norman's engraving, *Town of Falmouth, Burnt,* documents the 414 houses, stores, wharf buildings, courthouses, churches, and shops (three-quarters of the buildings standing in Falmouth) that were consumed by flames after Mowatt's bombardment. To the left, inhabitants flee the flames with their belongings loaded on carts.

Born in England, John Norman probably received training in the conventional bird's-eye perspective. Most likely basing his engraving on secondhand sources, he drew a meetinghouse bell tower in the shape of a round lighthouse and the octagonal windmill in a round form. Norman later collaborated with the mapmaker Osgood Carleton (20).

References: American Printmaking, 40; Willis, 506–23; Tooley, 468.

127

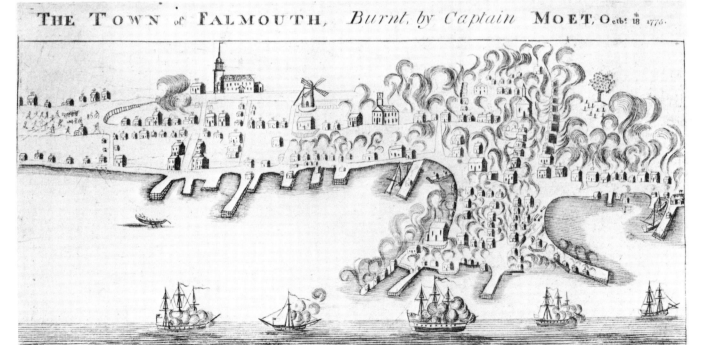

THE TOWN of FALMOUTH, *Burnt, by Captain* MOET, Octb! 18 1775.

128 DETAIL

128

Signals belonging to Merchants of Portland

Unknown artist

District of Maine, 1807

Watercolor and ink; 20 × 16⅛ in.

Maine Historical Society

To allow time for clearing wharf and warehouse space and for wholesalers to assemble for bidding, New England shipowners developed a system of signals by which lighthouse keepers communicated the number, type, and ownership of sailing vessels approaching from the open sea. *Signals belonging to Merchants of Portland* is a colored engraving that served as a roster or log of such signals used in Portland, Maine. A red flag indicated one ship; a red flag and red-and-white pennant, one ship and one brig. Other colors and ciphers indicated owners: for example, a flag with a red diamond in a white field signaled the ships of David Green. A sequence of four views of the harbor was drawn by the artist in central lunettes. The top one shows the coastline, harbor islands, and Portland Head lighthouse at a distance of several miles at sea. The second view shows the harbor islands and lighthouse as seen from a vantage

point in the harbor (probably the fort); the third, a view of Falmouth Neck; the fourth, a principal wharf with ships alongside. The third view, taken from what is now the Fore River, is the same seen in John Norman's *The Town of Falmouth, Burnt* (127). Completed in 1791, the Portland Head lighthouse was the earliest on the Maine coastline built by the United States Congress.

References: Smith, Thomas, 366; Bowen, Ashley, 1:184–85, 232.

129

Sketch of Cornwall Vally. Done by George Whitefield of the Chippeway Nation Aged 12 yrs

Catitugegwonhale (b. 1814)
Connecticut, 1826
Manuscript, ink and watercolor; 12½ × 8 in.
Scale 1:4,000
Litchfield Historical Society

130

N.Eastern view of Cornwall about 1 mile distant

John Warner Barber (1798–1885)
Connecticut, 1833
Manuscript, pencil; 6¾ × 9½ in., no. 50, field sketch series
The Connecticut Historical Society

131

N.Eastern view of South Cornwall 1 mile distant

John Warner Barber (1798–1885)
Connecticut, 1833
Ink and wash view; 3½ × 5 in.
The Connecticut Historical Society

The earliest comprehensive record of the New England landscape was provided by the historian and artist John Warner Barber of East Windsor, Connecticut (69). Between the years 1835 and 1840 Barber produced two books illustrated by several hundred landscape and architectural views of towns in Connecticut and Massachusetts. An antiquarian at heart, Barber was selective in what he portrayed. Railroad beds are seldom if ever seen in his views, although they were already in evidence on the landscape. Historic houses, sites, and burying grounds were favored over all other subjects.

The pencil sketch (130), wash drawing (131), and wood engraving depicting Cornwall, Connecticut, a town located in the Housatonic Valley in western Connecticut, represent the several stages by which Barber's field notes and sketches were worked into published form. Barber's half-finished sketch was drawn on the site and annotated with descriptive terms such as "Stone Wall," "Apple Trees," and "Colt's foot mountain." The pen-and-wash drawing, which is about half the size of the pencil sketch, was

prepared by Barber in his New Haven studio at some later point. This pen-and-wash drawing in turn guided a professional engraver who incised the end-grain surface of a buttonwood block that was used to produce the prints published in Barber's history.

Cornwall, Connecticut, was also the subject of a watercolor schoolboy map made about a decade before Barber's visit. *Sketch of Cornwall Vally. Done by George Whitefield of the Chippeway Nation* is the work of a twelve-year-old American Indian from the western Great Lakes region who attended the Foreign Mission School in Cornwall from 1825 to 1826. (Established in 1818 for the purpose of Christianizing native "Idolator[s]," the school had twenty-nine pupils in 1820 of whom nineteen were American Indians and six were Pacific Ocean natives.) Named "Catitugegwonhale" in Chippewa, Whitefield gained a reputation at the school for skill in penmanship and drawing. Visible on his map are stone walls (dotted lines), split-rail fences (zig-zag lines), pastures, cultivated fields, and orchards. The building occupied by the Foreign Mission School

129 DETAIL

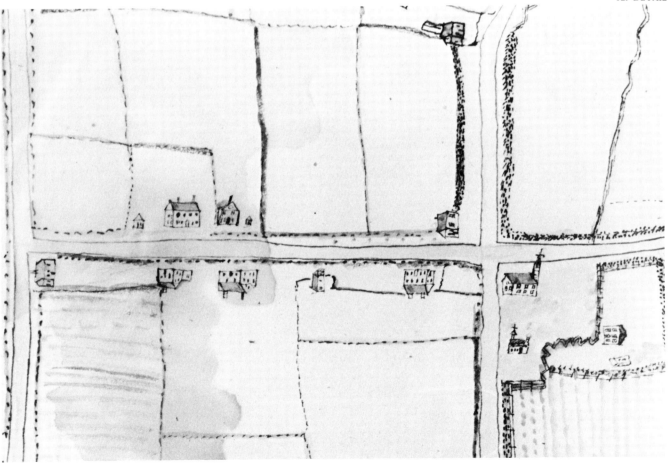

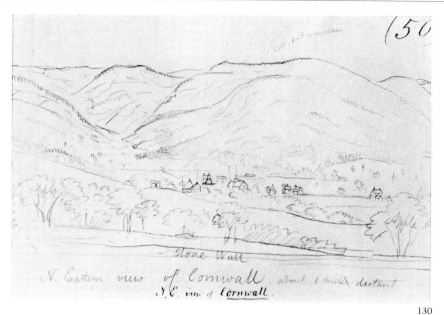

130

lies at the direct center of the map, surrounded by three small outbuildings and a checkerboard area of twelve cultivated plots called "The Garden" where every student at the school worked a piece of ground.

With the help of a nineteenth-century map of Cornwall identifying Colt's Foot Mountain, it is possible to locate the Whitefield map (scale 1:4000) within the Barber view (middleground scale approximately 1:8000). Correspondences can be seen in twin-chimney structures and in the 1790 meetinghouse. Surprisingly, however, in all other respects the two appear to illustrate entirely different scenes.

References: Barber, *Connecticut*, 466; Beers; Starr, 149–57; Krim.

131

Northeastern view of South Cornwall.

131A Barber, **Northeastern view of South Cornwall** 1836 woodcut.

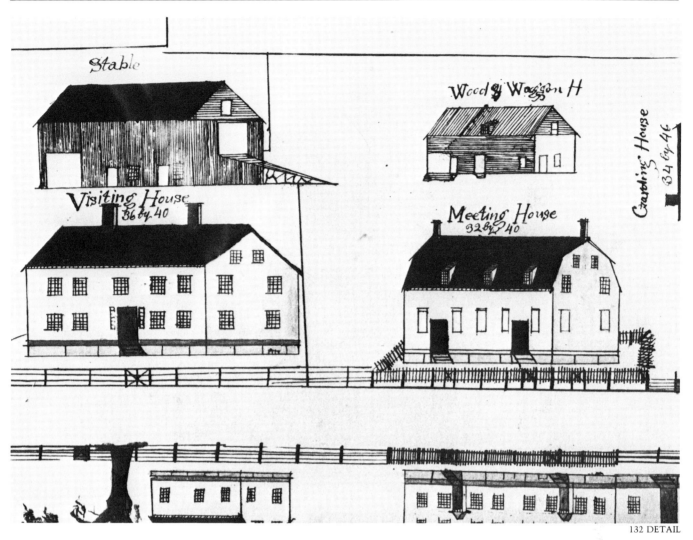

Stable

Visiting House
36 by 40

Wood & Waggon H

Meeting House
32 by 40

Carding House
34 by 46

132 DETAIL

132

A Plan of Alfred Maine August 28, 1845

Joshua H. Bussell

Maine, 1845

Manuscript, ink and watercolor; 22 × 39¼ in.

Scale approximately 1:350

Library of Congress

A Plan of Alfred Maine by Elder Joshua H. Bussell, dated August 1845, is a map of the Shaker community in Alfred by a prolific and influential Shaker mapmaker working just before the advent of photography. Designed as an administrative instrument, Bussell's map records the use, color, and dimensions of the principal buildings of the village, as well as the layout of roads and fences, the size and placement of trees, orchards, millponds, and fields. The village is divided into three clusters, each with an office, shop, and principal dwelling house, and each with outlying stables and barns. The single largest structure is a three-story dwelling house,

seventy-six by thirty-two feet in size, located in the south cluster. Adjacent dwellings include a "Boys House," "Visiting House," and "Nurse House." Work buildings and farm outbuildings testify to the self-sustaining nature of Shaker life and work: cider mill, wash house, dairy house, carding house, wood and wagon house, horse and sheep barn, turning mill, sawmill, grist mill, ox barn, and hog sty. The meetinghouse stands out as the only gambrel-roofed structure in the village; beside the meetinghouse is the "Ministrys Shop." With a few exceptions, buildings, fences, and trees are shown in their side or three-quarter elevations as they would be seen from the principal village road. Legends indicate building dimensions and function. Recent studies of Bussell's maps reveal that his cartography and iconography evolved in response to his exposure to outside influences. The most evident of these changes is his gradual shift from the cartographic plan used in the 1845 *Plan of Alfred* to an elevated bird's-eye perspective

as seen in his later maps. This shift was accompanied by a redefinition of the compass pointer, which is seen in the Alfred plan as a cartographic symbol but which in his later views is curiously located in the sky as a "flying" dimensional object.

Joshua Bussell, who learned mapmaking from earlier Shaker draftsmen such as David Buckingham and George Kendall, perpetuated and improved upon a self-taught tradition that was unique to the Shaker sect in America. Perhaps the only precedent to this tradition is the manor or estate maps (85), which were occasionally prepared by English or American cartographers for absentee English owners.

References: Emlen, "Early Drawings"; Emlen, "Shaker Maps."

Abbreviations used in references and end notes:

BL   British Library (British Museum)
BPL   Boston Public Library
CHS   Connecticut Historical Society
CSM   Colonial Society of Massachusetts
DAB   Dictionary of American Biography
DNB   Dictionary of National Biography
DSNEF   Dublin Seminar for New England Folklife
EIHC   Essex Institute Historical Collections
MHS   Massachusetts Historical Society
NEHGS   New England Historic Genealogical Society
NHHS   New Hampshire Historical Society
NHSL   New Hampshire State Library
OTNE   Old-Time New England
PRO   Public Records Office
RIHS   Rhode Island Historical Society

List of References Cited

Adams, James Truslow. *The Founding of New England.* Boston: Little, Brown, 1921.

Adams, Nathaniel. *Annals of Portsmouth.* Exeter, N.H.: Norris, 1825.

Albee, John. *New Castle, Historic and Picturesque.* Boston: Rand Avery, 1884.

American Printmaking: The First 150 Years. New York: Museum of Graphic Art, 1969.

Appleton's Cyclopedia of American Biography. Edited by James G. Wilson. 6 vols. New York: Appleton, 1888.

Austin, John Osborne. *The Genealogical Dictionary of Rhode Island.* Baltimore, Md.: Genealogical Publishing, 1969.

Ayres, Harral. *The Great Trail of New England.* Boston, 1940.

Babson, John J. *History of the Town of Gloucester.* Gloucester, Mass.: Procter, 1860.

Bacon, Oliver N. *A History of Natick.* Boston: Damrell, 1856.

Bailey, Joann Weeks. *A Guide to the History and Old Dwelling Places of Northwood, N.H.* Concord. N.H.: Capital, 1973.

Banks, Charles Edward. *The History of Martha's Vineyard.* 2 vols. Boston: Dean, 1911.

Barber, John Warner. *Historical Collections of Massachusetts.* Worcester, Mass.: Dorr, Howland, 1839.

———. *Connecticut Historical Collections.* 2d ed. New Haven: Durrie & Peck and J. W. Barber, 1836.

Batchelder, Charles H. *The Descendants of Nathaniel Batchelder of Hampton, New Hampshire.* Manuscript, NHHS Library, Concord, N.H., n.d.

Baylies, Francis. *An Historical Memoir of the Colony of New Plymouth.* 2 vols. Boston: Lunt, 1866.

Bedini, Silvio A. *Early American Scientific Instruments and Their Makers.* Washington, D.C.: Smithsonian, 1964.

Beers, F. W., et al. *County Atlas of Litchfield, Connecticut.* Litchfield, Conn.: Author, 1874.

Bell, Charles. *Facts Relating to the Early History of Chester, N.H.* Concord, N.H.: Lyon, 1863.

Bell, Charles Henry. *History of the Town of Exeter, New Hampshire.* Boston: J. E. Farwell, 1888.

Belknap, Henry Wycoff. *Artists and Craftsmen of Essex County Massachusetts.* Salem, Mass.: Essex Institute, 1927.

Belknap, Jeremy. *The History of New-Hampshire.* Vol. 1. 1784. Dover, N.H.: Stevens & Wadleigh, 1831.

———. *A New Map of New Hampshire.* Frontispiece in *The History of New-Hampshire.* Vol. 2. Boston: Thomas and Andrews, 1791.

———. *Belknap's New Hampshire; An Account of the State in 1792.* Edited by G. T. Lord. Facsimile of Dover 1812 ed. *The History of New-Hampshire.* Vol. 3. Hampton, N.H.: Peter E. Randall, 1973.

———. [Sketch plan of the part of Boston . . . overun by the fire of April, 1787.] Plan and letter reprinted in MHS *Collections,* 5th ser. 2 (1877):469–73.

Bentley, William. *The Diary of William Bentley, D.D.* 4 vols. Salem, Mass.: Essex Institute, 1905.

Black, Jeannette D. *The Blathwayt Atlas.* Vol. 1 *The Maps.* Vol. 2 *The Commentary.* Providence: Brown University, 1970, 1975.

———. "Mapping the English Colonies in North America: The Beginnings." In *The Compleat Plattmaker,* edited by Norman J. W. Thrower. Berkeley: University of California Press, 1978.

Blanchard, Joseph, and Langdon, Samuel. *Accurate map of his majesty's province of New Hampshire in New England.* Portsmouth, N.H., 1761.

Bolhouse, Gladys. "Incidents Through the Years at the Portsmouth Coal Mines." *Newport History* 40 (1967):1–21.

Bond, Henry. *Early Settlers of Watertown, Massachusetts.* 2 vols. Boston: Little, Brown, 1855.

Boston, City of. *A Volume of Records Relating to the Early History of Boston Containing Boston Marriages.* Boston: Municipal Printing Office, 1903.

Boston Engineering Department, City of. *List of Maps of Boston Published between 1600 and 1903.* Boston: Municipal Printing Office, 1903.

Boulind, Richard. "William Hack and the 'Description of New England' at Pilgrim Hall, Plymouth." In CSM *Publications* vol. 59. Boston: CSM, forthcoming. (Pages cited in references are from a 1976 printer's proof, iv–vii, 3–88.)

Bouton, Nathaniel. *History of Concord, N.H., 1725–1853.* Concord, N.H.: Sanborn, 1856.

Bowen, Ashley. *The Journals of Ashley Bowen of Marblehead.* 2 vols. Boston: CSM, 1973.

Bowen, Clarence W. *The Boundary Disputes of Connecticut.* Boston: Osgood, 1882.

Bradford, William. *History of Plymouth Plantation.* 2 vols. Boston: MHS, 1912.

Brigham, W. I. Tyler. *The History of the Brigham Family.* New York: Grafton, 1907.

British Library (British Museum), London. *Manuscript Maps, Charts and Plans and Technical Drawings in the British Museum.* 3 vols. London: Trustees of the Museum, 1861.

———. *Catalogue of Printed Maps, Charts and Plans.* 15 vols. London: British Museum, 1967.

Brodhead, J. Romeyn. "Observations respecting the two Ancient Maps of New Netherland, found in the Royal Archives at the Hague, in 1841." *New York State Historical Society Proceedings 1845* (1846):182–92.

Buell, Abel. *A New and Correct Map of the United States of North America.* New Haven, 1783.

Cabot, Harriet R. *Handbook of the Bostonian Society.* Boston: Bostonian Society, 1979.

Cady, John Hutchings. *The Civic and Architectural Development of Providence.* Providence: Book Shop, 1957.

Campbell, Tony. "The Drapers' Company and Its School of Seventeenth-Century Chart-Makers." In *My Head Is a Map: Essays and Memoirs in Honour of R. V. Tooley.* Edited by Helen Wallis and Sarah Tyacke. London, 1973.

———. "New Light on the Jansson-Visscher Maps of New England." *The Map Collectors' Circle* 24 (1965):3–46.

Candee, Richard M. "The Water Powered Sawmills of the Piscataqua." *OTNE* 60 (1970):131–49.

———. "Land Surveys of William and John Godsoe of Kittery, Maine: 1689–1769." *Annual Proceedings, DSNEF* (1980): *New England Prospect,* in press.

Carpenter, Charles H., Jr. "Early Dated Scrimshaw." *Magazine Antiques* 102 (September 1972):414–19.

Carrigain, Philip, Jr. *Map of New Hampshire. 1816.*

Carter, N. F., and Fowler, T. L. *History of Pembroke, New Hampshire, 1730–1895.* 2 vols. Concord, N.H.: Republican, 1895.

Catalogue of the Maps and Charts in the Library of Harvard University. Cambridge, Mass.: Metcalf, 1831.

Chamberlain, Mellen. *A Documentary History of Chelsea.* 2 vols. Boston: MHS, 1908.

Chambers's Encyclopaedia. Oxford, England: Pergamon Press, 1967.

Chapin, Howard Millar. *Cartography of Rhode Island.* Providence, 1915.

———. *Documentary History of Rhode Island.* 2 vols. Providence: Preston and Rounds, 1916–1919.

———. *Check List of Maps of Rhode Island.* Providence: Preston, 1918. Also in RIHS *Collections* 11 (1918):47–98.

Chapple, William D. "The Public Service of John Endecott in the Massachusetts Bay Colony." *EIHC* 65, (October 1929):403–47.

Charnock, John. *Biographia Navalis.* 6 vols. London: R. Faulder, 1794–1798.

Chase, George W. *History of Haverhill, Mass.* Haverhill, Mass.: Chase, 1861.

Chase, Levi B. "Interpretation of Woodward's and Saffery's *Map* of 1642 or the Earliest Bay Path." Quinabaug Historical Society *Leaflets,* vol. 1, no. 7, 1901.

Chatterton, E. Keble. *Captain John Smith.* New York: Harper, 1927.

Childs Gallery, Boston. "a vew of Boston." Typescript, n.d.

Clark, William R. *A Discourse on the Formation and Progress of the First Methodist Episcopal Church in Lynn.* Boston: Rand & Avery, 1859.

Clarke, George K. *History of Needham.* Cambridge, Mass.: Harvard University Press, 1912.

Coffin, Joshua. *A Sketch of the History of Newbury, Newburyport, and West Newbury.* Boston: Drake, 1845.

Concord Town Records. 1732–1820. Concord, N.H., 1894.

Convers, Francis. *An Historical Sketch of Watertown.* Cambridge, Mass.: Metcalf, 1830.

Crone, G. R. "John Green. Notes on a Neglected Eighteenth Century Geographer and Cartographer." *Imago Mundi* 6 (1949):85–91.

———. "Further Notes on Bradock Mead, alias John Green, an Eighteenth Century Cartographer." *Imago Mundi* 8 (1951):69–70.

Crowell, Robert. *History of the Town of Essex.* Essex, Mass.: Town of Essex, 1868.

Cumming, William P. *British Maps of Colonial America.* Chicago: University of Chicago Press, 1974.

———. "The Colonial Charting of the Massachusetts Coast." In *Seafaring in Colonial Massachusetts.* Boston: CSM, 1980, pp. 67–118.

Currier, John J. *Ould Newbury.* Boston: Damrell, 1896.

———. *History of Newbury, Mass., 1635–1902.* Boston: Damrell, 1902.

———. *History of Newburyport, Mass., 1764–1905.* Newburyport, Mass.: Author, 1906.

Danforth, Nicholas, and Danforth, William. *Danforth Genealogy.* Boston: Pope, 1902.

Danforth, Susan. "Osgood Carleton, Mapmaker." Paper read at New England Prospect: Maps, Place Names, and the Historical Landscape, June 1980, DSNEF, Dublin, N.H.

Deane, Charles. "Notes on Hubbard's Map of New England." MHS *Proceedings,* 2d. ser. 4 (1887–1889):13–21.

Dictionary of American Biography. 20 vols. New York: Scribner, 1944–1973.

Dictionary of National Biography. 22 vols. London: Oxford, 1949–1950.

Dorchester Antiquarian and Historical Society. *History of the Town of Dorchester, Mass.* Boston: Ebenezer Clapp, Jr., 1859.

Douglass, William. *A Summary, Historical and Political, Of the . . . British Settlements in North America.* 2 vols. Boston, 1749–1752.

Dow, Joseph. *History of the Town of Hampton, New Hampshire.* Salem, Mass: Salem Press, 1893.

Downing, Antoinette. "History of the Friends Meeting House in Newport, R.I." *Newport History* 41 (Fall 1968):140–41.

du Mont, John S. *American Engraved Powder Horns: The Golden Age, 1755–1783.* Canaan, N.H.: Phoenix, 1978.

Dudley, Robert. "Carta particolare della nuova Belgia." In *Dell' Arcano del Mare.* Florence, Italy, 1646.

Eaton, Francis B. *History of Candia.* Manchester, N.H.: Farmer, 1852.

Edmonds, John H. "Captain Thomas Pound, Pilot, Pirate, Cartographer, and Captain in the Royal Navy." CSM *Transactions* 20 (1917–1920):24–84.

Ellsworth, John E. *Simsbury, Being a Brief Historical Sketch of Ancient and Modern Simsbury, 1642–1935.* Hartford, Conn.: Simsbury Committee, 1935.

Emlen, Robert P. "Early Drawings of Elder Joshua Bussell." *Magazine Antiques* 113 (March 1978):632–37.

———. "Shaker Village Maps in New England." Paper read at New England Prospect: Maps, Place Names, and the Historical Landscape, June 1980, DSNEF, Dublin, N.H.

Endicott, Charles M. *Memoir of John Endecott.* Salem, Mass.: 1847.

"Essay on the Laying Out of Towns." MHS *Collections,* 5th ser. 1 (1871):474–80.

Failey, Dean F. *Long Island Is My Nation: The Decorative Arts and Craftsmen, 1640–1830.* Setauket, L.I.: Society for the Preservation of Long Island Antiquities, 1976.

Felt, Joseph B. *History of Ipswich, Essex and Hamilton.* Cambridge, Mass.: Folsom, 1834.

Fisher, Philip A. "The Fisher Family." *Dedham Historical Register* 3 (October 1892):187–92.

Fiske, John. *New England and New France.* Cambridge, Mass.: Riverside Press, 1902.

French, Frederic. *A Plan of Chelmsford protracted by a Scale of 200 rods to an Inch Surveyed Nov 1794.* Mass. Archives, The State House, Boston, Mass.

Frost, Norman S. *Frost Genealogy in Five Families.* West Newton, Mass.: Frost Family Association, 1926.

Fuller, Oliver P. *History of Warwick, R.I.* Providence: Angell, 1875.

Ganong, William F. "The Origin of the Place-names Acadia and Norumbega." The Royal Society of Canada *Proceedings and Transactions,* vol. 11, sect. 2, 1917.

———. "Crucial Maps in the Early Cartography and Place-Nomenclature of the Atlantic Coast of Canada, III." The Royal Society of Canada *Proceedings and Transactions,* vol. 25, sect. 2, 1931.

Garvan, Anthony N. B. *Architecture and Town Planning in Colonial Connecticut.* New Haven: Yale University Press, 1971.

Gloucester, Mass. *Vital Records of Gloucester, Mass.* 2 vols. Topsfield, Mass.: Topsfield Historical Society, 1917.

Goodell, Abner C., Jr. "Fac-Simile of the Earliest Known Chart of Boston Harbor." BPL *Bulletin* n.s. 12 (1893):91–92. Also in MHS *Proceedings*, 2d ser. 8 (1893):228–30.

Granscay, S. V. *American Engraved Powder Horns.* New York: Metropolitan Museum of Art, 1945.

Green, Samuel A. "Some Remarks on the Waters-Winthrop Map." MHS *Proceedings*, 2d ser. 7 (1892):335–38.

Hales, John G. *Plan of the Town of Chelmsford in the County of Middlesex Surveyed in 1831 by John G. Hales.* Mass. Archives, The State House, Boston, Mass.

Hammett, Charles E., Jr., and Turner, George F. *Road Map of the Island of Rhode Island or Aquidneck.* Lithograph of Sarony & Major, 1849.

Hatch, Louis C. *Maine, a History.* 1919. Reprint. Somersworth, N.H.: New Hampshire Publishing, 1974.

Hayward, John. *Gazetteer of Vermont.* Boston: Tappan, 1849.

Hazlett, Charles A. *History of Rockingham County, N.H. and Representative Citizens.* Chicago: Richmond, 1915.

Hemenway, Abby M., ed. *Vermont Historical Gazetteer.* 5 vols. Burlington, Vt.: Privately Printed, 1867–1891.

Heylyn, Peter. *Cosmographie in Four Books. Containing the Chorographie and Historie of the Whole World.* London: Seile, 1652.

Hine, Orlo D. *Early Lebanon.* Hartford, Conn.: Brainard, 1880.

Historical Catalogue of Brown University, 1764–1904. Providence: Brown University, 1905.

Hitchings, Sinclair. "Guarding the New England Coast: The Naval Career of Cyprian Southack." *Seafaring in Colonial Massachusetts.* Boston: CSM, 1980, pp. 43–66.

Hodges, George. *Holderness, An Account of the Beginnings of a New Hampshire Town.* Boston: Houghton Mifflin, 1907.

Holland, Josiah Gilbert. *History of Western Massachusetts.* 2 vols. Springfield, Mass.: Bowles, 1855.

Holman, Richard B. "John Foster's Woodcut Map of New England." *Printing and Graphic Arts* 8 (1960):53–93.

———. "William Burgis." *Boston Prints and Printmakers.* Boston: CSM, 1975.

Hudson, Alfred Sereno. *The History of Sudbury, Massachusetts.* Sudbury, Mass.: Bodgett, 1889.

Huish, Marcus. *Samplers and Tapestry Embroideries.* 1900. Reprint. New York: Dover, 1970.

Hurd, D. Hamilton. *History of Rockingham & Stafford Counties N.H.* Philadelphia: Lewis, 1882.

Isham, Norman. "Jireh Bull Garrison House." RIHS *Collections* 11, no. 1 (January 1918):2–11.

Jenney, Charles Francis. "Northerly Part of Ancient Line between Dedham and Dorchester." *Dedham Historical Register* 1 (July 1890):94–95.

Jennings, Francis. *Invasion of America: Indians, Colonialism, and the Cant of Conquest.* New York: W. W. Norton, 1975.

"JESSE STARr" (Maphorn, Boston, 1775). Illustrated in MHS *Proceedings* 2d ser. 52 (June 1919):334.

Judd, Sylvester. *History of Hadley.* Springfield, Mass.: Hunting, 1905.

Kelly, J. Frederick. *Early Connecticut Meeting Houses.* 2 vols. New York: Columbia University Press, 1948.

Kensington, N.H. *A plan of the Town of Kensington taken by the Selectmen of said Town in the year 1805 agreeable to an Act passed in the General Court December 30th 1803.* Concord, N.H.:NHSL.

Keuning, Johannes. "Blaeu's Atlas." *Imago Mundi* 14 (1959):74–88.

Kevitt, Chester B. *General Solomon Lovell and the Penobscot Expedition.* Weymouth, Mass.: Historical Commission, 1976.

Kittery Town Records. Vols. 1 and 2. Town Clerk's Office, Kittery, Maine.

Klemp, Egon. *America in Maps Dating from 1500 to 1846.* London: Holmes, 1976.

Kneeland, Abner. *Weare, In the County of Hilsborough and State of New Hampshire 1805.* Manuscript at NHSL, Concord, N.H.

Krim, Arthur J. "Graphic Landscapes of Massachusetts, 1835–1845." Paper delivered to the New England College English Association at Clark University, 7 April 1979.

Lamson, Alvan. *A History of the First Church and Parish in Dedham.* Dedham, Mass.: Mann, 1839.

Lancaster, Daniel. *History of Gilmanton, N.H.* Gilmanton, N.H.: Prescott, 1845.

Lane, Samuel. *A Plan of Some part of the Township of Holderness . . . 1752.* Manuscript at NHHS Library, Concord, N.H.

———. *A Journal for the Years 1739–1803.* Concord, N.H.: NHHS, 1937.

Leonard, Mary Hall. *Mattapoisett and Old Rochester, Mass.* New York: Grafton, 1907.

Lewis, Alonzo. *History of Lynn.* Boston: Eastburn, 1829.

———. *Map of Lynn and Saugus surveyed and drawn by Alonzo Lewis 1829.* Lithograph by James Eddy, Pendleton's Lithography, Boston.

Linton, W. J. *The history of wood-engraving in America.* Boston: Estes & Lauriat, 1882.

Little, Nina Fletcher. *American Decorative Wall Painting 1700–1850.* New York: Dutton, 1972.

———. *Country Arts in Early American Homes.* New York: Dutton, 1975.

Little, William. *The History of Weare, N.H., 1735–1888.* Lowell, Mass.: Huse, 1888.

Lockridge, Kenneth A. *A New England Town the First Hundred Years.* New York: Norton, 1970.

Lovett, John. Map of Salem and Beverly by Lovett, 1817. Essex Institute Library, Salem, Mass., #912.7446 B57 L1.

Lyford, James O., ed. *History of Concord, N.H.* 2 vols. Concord, N.H.: Rumford, 1903.

Lyman, Dean B., Jr. *An Atlas of Old New Haven or "The Nine Squares."* New Haven, Scranton, 1929.

McDuffie, Franklin. *History of the Town of Rochester, N.H., 1722–1890.* 2 vols. Manchester, N.H.: Clarke, 1892.

McManis, Douglas R. *European Impressions of the New England Coast, 1497–1620.* Chicago: University of Chicago Press, 1972.

"Map of Eastern Massachusetts." MHS *Proceedings*, 2d ser. 1 (June 1884):211–16.

A Map of the most Inhabited part of New England, containing the Provinces of Massachusetts Bay and New Hampshire with the Colonies of Conecticut and Rhode Island. Printed for Carrington Bowles, at No. 69 in St. Pauls Church Yard London, January 1771.

Map showing the Pawtuxet Lands, and Houses. From a deed of 1661. Reduced facsimile in *Documentary History of Rhode Island,* by Howard M. Chapin. 2 vols. Providence: Preston, 1916; and in RIHS *Collections* 21–25 (1928–1932):48–49.

Marshall, Douglas W. *John Montresor in America: Eighteenth-Century Military Maps.* Broadside of an exhibition at the University of Michigan Museum of Art arranged by the William L. Clements Library. Ann Arbor, Michigan, 1979.

Marshall, Douglas W., and Peckham, Howard. *Campaigns of the American Revolution; An Atlas of American Maps.* Ann Arbor: University of Michigan Press, 1975.

Massachusetts Archives. Card catalogue of manuscript maps and plans. State House, Boston, Mass.

Massachusetts Bay Colony. *Records of the Governor and Company of the Massachusetts Bay in New England.* Edited by Nathaniel B. Shurtleff. 5 vols. in 6. Boston: William White, 1853–1854.

Massachusetts, Province of. *The Acts and Resolves of the Massachusetts Bay Province, 1708–1720.* Vol. 9. Boston: Wright, 1902.

Mayo, Lawrence S. *John Endecott: A Biography.* Cambridge, Mass.: Harvard University Press, 1936.

Meriden. N.H. *One Hundredth Anniversary of the Congregational Church.* Lebanon, N.H.: Free Press, 1880.

Merrill, Georgia Drew. *History of Carroll County, N.H.* Somersworth, N.H.: New Hampshire Publishing, 1871.

Merrill, Phinehas. *Scholar's Guide to Arithmetic.* Exeter, N.H., 1793, 1794; Portsmouth, N.H.: 1798; Exeter, N.H., 1802.

Merrill, Phinehas, Inventory of the estate of. Stratham, N.H.: Rockingham County Probate Records, no. 9012.

Merrill, Samuel. *A Merrill Memorial: An Account of the Descendants of Nathaniel Merrill, an Early Settler of Newbury, Mass.* Cambridge, Mass., 1917–1928.

Metcalf, John G. *Annals of the Town of Mendon.* Providence: Freeman, 1880.

Monahon, Eleanore Bradford. "A New Look at the Jireh Bull Excavation." *Rhode Island History* 20, no. 1 (January 1961):13–24.

Moore, J. Bailey. *History of the Town of Candia.* Manchester, N.H.: Browne, 1893.

More, Henry. "Sketch of John Warner Barber." In *The Picture Preacher,* by John W. Barber. New Haven: More, 1880, pp. 14–22.

Morison, Samuel E. *The European Discovery of America. The Northern Voyages, A.D. 500–1600.* New York: Oxford, 1971.

Morse, C. F. *Historical Discourse delivered at Atkinson, N.H.* Lawrence, Mass.: Merrill, 1875.

Murray, James A. H., ed. *A New English Dictionary on Historical Principles.* 10 vols. in 12. Oxford: Clarendon Press, 1888–1928.

Nelson, Charles B. *History of Stratham, New Hampshire, 1631–1900.* Somersworth, N.H.: New Hampshire Publishing, 1965.

New Hampshire. *Laws of New Hampshire. Vol. 7. Second Constitution, 1801–1811. Vol. 8. 1811–1820.* Concord, N.H.: Evans, 1918.

"A New Survey of the Harbour of Boston in New England." *English Pilot,* 4th part. London, 1707.

North-Eastern Approaches. Newsletter, Maine State Museum 2, no. 2 (1978):1–2.

Notes, Historical, Descriptive and Personal of Livermore, Maine. Portland, Me.: Bailey, 1874.

O'Brien, Donald C. "Abner Reed: A Connecticut Engraver." CHS *Bulletin* 44, no. 1 (1 January 1979):1–16.

Palfrey, John Gorham. *A Compendious History of the First Century of New England.* 3 vols. Boston: Shepard, 1872.

Parker, Benjamin F. *History of Wolfeborough, New Hampshire.* Wolfeborough, N.H.: Town of Wolfeborough, 1901.

Parsons, L. B. *History of the Town of Rye, N.H.* Concord, N.H.: Rumford, 1905.

Patten, Matthew. *The Diary of Matthew Patten of Beford, N.H.* Concord, N.H.: Rumford, 1903.

Paullin, Charles O., and Wright, John K. *Atlas of the Historical Geography of the United States.* Washington, D.C.: Carnegie Institution and American Geographical Society, 1932.

Peabody, Selim Hobart. *Peabody Genealogy.* Boston: Pope, 1909.

Pettingell, Charles I. "The West Parish of Salisbury, Massachusetts, and the Rocky Hill Meetinghouse." *OTNE* 57, no. 2 (October–December 1966):29–45.

Phelps, Noah A. *History of Simsbury, Granby and Canton from 1642 to 1845.* Hartford, Conn.: Case, Tiffany, 1845.

Phillips, P. Lee. *A List of Maps of America in the Library of Congress.* Washington, D.C.: Government Printing Office, 1901.

Pickles, John D. *Centennial Anniversary of the First Methodist Episcopal Church.* Lynn, Mass., 1891.

Pitkin, Albert P. *Pitkin Family of America.* Hartford, Conn.: Case, Lockwood, 1887.

Pound, Thomas. *A New Mapp of New England.* 1691. Reduced photo engraving. CSM *Transactions* 20 (1917–1919):42.

"Powder Horn Maps." *Mapline,* no. 4 (1976). Newberry Library, Chicago, Ill.

"Powder Horn with View of Providence Cut in 1777 by Charles Hewit." RIHS *Collections* 21, no. 4 (October 1928):124–25.

Powell, Sumner Chilton. *Puritan Village: The Formation of a New England Town.* Middletown, Conn.: Wesleyan, 1963.

Prescott, William. "Report on the alterations of the Channel of Merrimack River. Read before the New Hampshire Historical Society at its Annual Meeting, in June, 1853." NHHS *Collections* 7 (1863):433–40.

———. *The Prescott Memorial: or a Genealogical Memoir of the Prescott Families in America.* Boston: Dutton, 1870.

"PROVIDENCE F STEPHEN AVERY his horn." Illustrated in RIHS *Collections* 11, no. 3 (July 1918):84–85, 88–89.

Public Records Office, London. *Maps and Plans in the Public Records Office.* 2 vols. Edited by P. A. Penfold. London: His Majesty's Stationery Office, 1974.

Purchas, Samuel. *Hakluytus Posthumos or Purchas His Pilgrims.* 20 vols. Glasgow: MacLehose, 1625.

Reps, John W. "Boston by Bostonians: The Printed Plans and Views of the Colonial City by its Artists, Cartographers, Engravers, and Publishers." *Boston Prints and Printmakers, 1670–1775.* Boston: CSM, 1973.

Paul Revere's Boston: 1735–1818. Boston: Museum of Fine Arts, 1975.

Richeson, A. W. *English Land Measuring to 1800: Instruments and Practices.* Cambridge, Mass.: MIT Press, 1966.

Rockport, Mass. *Vital Records of Rockport, Massachusetts,* Salem: Essex Institute, 1924.

Rose, Harold W. *The Colonial Houses of Worship in America.* New York: Hastings, 1963.

Ryder, Alice A. *Lands of Sippican.* New Bedford, Mass.: Reynolds, 1934.

Sanderson, Edmund L. *Waltham as a Precinct of Watertown.* Waltham, Mass.: Waltham Historical Society Publication Number 5, 1936.

"Sandwich, N.H." Collection of negative newsclippings, and so on. NEHGS Library, Boston, Mass.

Sawyer, Roland D. *History of Kensington, N.H.* 1874. Reprint. Farmington, Me.: Knowlton, 1946.

Schenck, Elizabeth H. *The History of Fairfield, Fairfield County, Connecticut.* 2 vols. New York: Privately Printed, 1889–1905.

Seelye, John. *Prophetic Waters: The River in Early American Life and Literature.* New York: Oxford, 1977.

Shattuck, Lemuel. *Memorials of the Descendants of William Shattuck.* Boston: Dutton, 1855.

"Ship Registers of the District of Newburyport." *EIHC* 71 (April 1935):177.

Shirley, William. "Instructions given by William Shirley, Governor of Massachusetts, to William Pepperell." MHS *Collections* Vol. 1 (1792). Boston, 1806, pp. 5–17.

Sinnott, Edmund W. *Meetinghouse & Church in Early New England.* New York: McGraw-Hill, 1963.

Skelton, R. A. *Decorative and Printed Maps of the Fifteenth to Eighteenth Centuries.* London: Staples Press, 1952.

Smart, Charles E. *The Makers of Surveying Instruments in America since 1700.* Troy, N.Y.: Regal, 1962.

Smibert, John. *The Notebook of John Smibert.* Boston: MHS, 1969.

Smith, Edgar Crosby. "Maine Map-Makers and Their Maps I: Osgood Carleton." *Sprague's Journal of Maine History* 2, no. 1 (May 1914):3–9.

Smith, E. Vale. *History of Newburyport*. Newburyport, Mass., 1854.

Smith, Frank. *A History of Dedham, Massachusetts*. Dedham, Mass.: Transcript, 1936.

Smith, John. *Captain John Smith's America: Selections from His Writings*, edited by John Lankford. New York: Harper, 1967.

Smith, Thomas. *Journals of Rev. Thomas Smith*, edited by William Willis. Portland, Me.: Bailey, 1849.

Smith, Thomas R. "Manuscript and Printed Sea Charts in Seventeenth-Century London: The Case of the Thames School." In *The Compleat Plattmaker*, edited by J. W. Thrower. Berkeley: University of California Press, 1978.

Southack, Cyprian. *The New England Coasting Pilot*. Boston, 1719–1733.

Starr, Edward B. *History of Cornwall, Connecticut*. New Haven: Tuttle, 1926.

Stevens, Henry, and Tree, Roland. "Comparative Cartography: . . . Maps and Charts of the American Continent Published in Great Britain during the Years 1600–1850." *Map Collectors Circle* 39 (1967):305–63.

Stiles, Ezra. *Extracts from the Itineraries, 1755–1794*. Edited by F. B. Dexter. New Haven: Yale University Press, 1916.

Stiles, Henry R. *History and Genealogies of Ancient Windsor, Connecticut*. 2 vols. Hartford, Conn.: Case, Lockwood & Brainard, 1891–1892.

Stokes, I. N. Phelps. *The Iconography of Manhattan-Island*. 6 vols. New York, 1915–1928.

Suffolk County, Mass. *Superior Court Records* Maps (Books 1 and 2). Suffolk County Court House, Boston.

Thompson, Edmund. *Maps of Connecticut before the year 1800*. Windham, Conn.: Hawthorn House, 1940.

Tooley, Ronald V. *Dictionary of Mapmakers*. Tring, Hertfordshire, England: Map Collector, 1979.

"Topography and History of Rochester, Mass. 1815." *MHS Collections*, 2d ser. 4 (1816):250–67.

Trumbull, Benjamin. *A Complete History of Connecticut, Civil and Ecclesiastical*. 1797. 2 vols. New London, Conn.: H. D. Utley, 1898.

Trumbull, J. Hammond. ". . . description of the earliest known chart of the harbor." In *The Memorial History of Boston*, by Justin Winsor. 4 vols. Boston: Osgood, 1881.

———. Correspondence. William Willis, Edward Ballard, and J. Hammond Trumbull. 1864. Maine Historical Society.

Turner, Henry E. *Greene's of Warwick in Colonial History*. Newport, R.I.: Davis, 1877.

Tuttle, Julius H. "Early Manuscript Maps of New England." *CSM Proceedings* 17 (March 1913):111–15.

Van Dusen, Albert E. *Puritans Against the Wilderness: Connecticut History to 1763*. Chester, Conn.: Pequot, 1975.

Vaughan, Alden T. *New England Frontier: Puritans and Indians, 1620–1675*. Boston: Little, Brown, 1965.

Verner, Coolie. "The Fry and Jefferson map." *Imago Mundi* 21 (1967).

———. "John Seller and the Chart Trade in Seventeenth-Century England." In *The Compleat Plattmaker*, edited by Norman J. W. Thrower. Berkeley: University of California Press, 1978.

Voye, Nancy D., ed. *Massachusetts Officers in the French and Indian Wars, 1748–1763*. Boston: Society of Colonial Wars in the Commonwealth of Massachusetts, 1975.

Waite, Emma F. "William Price of Boston: Map-Maker, Merchant and Churchman." *OTNE* 46, no. 2 (October–December 1956):52–56.

Walker, Hovenden, *An Exact Draught of Bostone harbour, with a Survey of most of the Islands about it 1711*. Manuscript at the British Library, London. 1883 facsimile at BPL. Reproduced in Chamberlain, I:1.

Waterbury, Theodore E. "John P. Newell 1832?–1898." *Newport History* 41, no. 2 (1968):67–73.

Waters, Thomas F. *Ipswich in the Massachusetts Bay Colony*. 2 vols. Ipswich, Mass.: Ipswich Historical Society, 1917.

Waters, Wilson. *History of Chelmsford, Mass*. Lowell, Mass.: Courier, 1917.

Watertown, Mass. *Watertown Records*. Vol 3. Watertown, Mass.: Barker, 1900.

Webb, Nathaniel. *Plan of the Third Society in Lebanon called Goshen . . . Surveyed Nov. 1769 & Aug. 1770 by Nath¹ Webb, County Surveyor*. Blueprint copy of privately owned manuscript, CHS, Hartford, Conn.

Wells, Daniel W., and Wells, Reuben F. *History of Hatfield*. Springfield, Mass.: Gibbons, 1910.

Wheat, James Clements, and Brun, Christian F. *Maps and Charts Published in America Before 1800: A Bibliography*. New Haven: Yale University Press, 1969.

Wheeler, Ruth R. *Concord: Climate for Freedom*. Concord, Mass.: Concord Antiquarian Society, 1967.

Whitehill, Walter M. *Boston: A Topographical History*. Cambridge, Mass.: Harvard University Press, 1959.

Williams, Roger. "Seven Letters of Roger Williams." *MHS Collections*, 3d ser, 1 (1825–1830):159–61.

Willis, William. *History of Portland*. Portland, Me.: Day, Fraser, 1831.

Winsor, Justin, ed. *Narrative and Critical History of America*. 8 vols. Boston and New York: Houghton Mifflin, 1884–1889.

———. *The Kohl Collection of Early Maps*. Washington, D.C.: Government Printing Office, 1904.

———. *The Memorial History of Boston*. 4 vols. Boston: Osgood, 1885.

Winthrop, John. *Winthrop Papers*. Vol. 2. 1623–1630. Boston: MHS, 1931.

Wood, William. *Nevv Englands Prospect. A true, lively, and experimentall description of that part of America, commonly called Nevv England*. London: Tho. Cotes for John Bellamie, 1634. Facsimile edition edited by E. M. Boynton, Boston, 1897.

Woodward, David. "The Foster woodcut map controversy: a further examination of the evidence." *Imago Mundi* 21 (1968):52–61.

Wytfliet, Cornelius. *Descriptionis Ptolemaicae Augmentum*. London, 1603. Copy in the Library of the Boston Athenaeum.

Index of Place Names

Figures indicate catalogue entries.

1 DETAIL

Photo Credits